THE CRANE MAKERS OF CARLISLE

The Cowans, Sheldon Story

A Nostalgia Road Publication

The HERITAGE series

is produced under licence by

Nostalgia Road Publications Ltd.
Unit 6, Chancel Place
Shap Road Industrial Estate,
Kendal, Cumbria - LA9 6NZ
Tel. 01539 738832 - Fax: 01539 730075

designed and published by
Trans-Pennine Publishing Ltd.
PO Box 10,
Appleby-in-Westmorland, Cumbria, CA16 6FA
Tel. 017683 51053 Fax. 017683 53558
e-mail: admin@transpenninepublishing.co.uk

and printed by
Kent Valley Colour Printers Ltd.
Kendal, Cumbria. 01539 741344

Front Cover: *A 15-ton Cowans, Sheldon steam breakdown crane ends its days with British Railways Midland Region as RS1025/15, and paired to an 8-ton match truck DM 116953. It was built at Carlisle in 1899 for the Midland Railway and was scrapped by BR in 1961. It spent its early working life in Bristoll finished its days at Bletchley MPD where, in the background an ex-LMS Stannier 2-6-2T No.40080 can be seen*

Rear Cover Top: *In this watercolour painting from the 19th Century, the original Woodbank Works of Cowans, Sheldon & Co. can be seen.*

Rear Cover Centre: *This lightweight hand-operated crane was one of those built by Cowans, Sheldon during World War II for emergency repair work. It is pictured in 1993 on the private garden railway of Sir William McAlpine at Henley.* Alan Earnshaw

Rear Cover Bottom: *An imposing aerial view from the 1950s, showing the St. Nicholas Works. Note how complex and compact the site was, with every inch of space being put to good use.*

Opposite: *The facade of the St. Nicholas Works from a very tranquil London Road in 1949, contrast the scene with the same spot today!*

Throughout the railway and maritime world, the name of Cowans, Sheldon & Co., has long been synonymous with quality products; from breakdown cranes to dock cranes, and from water columns to turntables, the Carlisle-based engineers led where others followed. However, the remarkable story of this world-leading firm is little known, and what went on behind the high brick walls at St. Nicholas was a mystery to both railway enthusiasts and the folk of Carlisle alike. Yet this is a situation that I will now attempt to redress, as I record the story of this remarkable firm who were simply known in Carlisle as The Crane-Makers.

The development of this book has passed through a long period of gestation, and it is over 15 years since I started to research the remarkable story of the firm. Throughout the project the staff at Cowans Boyd (both prior to their departure from the St. Nicholas Works and since) have ably assisted me. On closure of the manufacturing operations in Carlisle, and the transfer of that work to Tyneside, a design office was set up in The Carlisle Enterprise Centre in James Street. From here several members of staff contributed information towards the book. I must especially record my thanks to Mike Keddy who has watched the project grow from a germ of an idea to a completed book.

In 1996 Cowans Boyd finally withdrew from operations in the Border City, but the team of designers and draughtsmen formed a new company Des-Cad, who have continued the fine design traditions of the old company.

Recording the heritage of great companies like Cowans, Sheldon is an important part of our social history, because once these firms have gone, they have gone forever. It was with mixed emotions that the old works were demolished to make way for a shopping complex, but in the midst of falling bricks and flying glass a little bit of the city's history was thankfully preserved.

During the course of demolition I happened to be presenting a programme on BBC Radio Cumbria, when I received an urgent request from Mike Keddy to go down to the site, because the workers had discovered an old safe full of glass-plate negatives. With the kind permission of the contractors, Mountelm Ltd., I was allowed to retrieve these photographs and some other old records (including the works order book) that had been thrown into a skip to burn. In due course the items were deposited in three main museums. The first of these was the Carlisle's Tullie House Museum, the second was the Royal Naval Museum in Portsmouth, with the third being Beamish, the North of England Open Air Museum.

Edward P.
Sheldon

James Losh

John Cowans

The progressive dissemination of the material that was saved has been a mammoth task, but it is this that serves as the basis for this brief introduction to the fascinating story of Cowans, Sheldon. However, it is a story that could not have been told without the very kind efforts of a large number of people. Though the firm of Cowans, Sheldon, and latterly Cowans Boyd has long been associated with Carlisle, its origins can be traced directly back to North East England. The two founders, John Cowans and Edward Pattinson Sheldon, were both born in 'the cradle of the railways' and they began their careers as apprentices with Robert Stephenson & Co. Here their friendship developed, and along with one of the older apprentices, William Bouch, they became known in the Tyneside works as 'an irrepressible trio'. As their apprenticeship progressed, Stephenson recognised that they each had talents deserving of a wider audience and actively encouraged them to look at areas where they might develop their inventive skills.

In 1839 Bouch began advertising for business in his own right, yet before long he had taken up an appointment with the Stockton & Darlington Railway, and we are unsure about the exact nature of his early ventures. Meanwhile, both Cowans and Sheldon had also resolved to form their own business. The two men had contrasting temperaments that were to serve as an ideal mixture for a successful partnership; with the cautious, meticulous nature of Sheldon being balanced by the enthusiastic optimism of Cowans.

It would have seemed to be logical for them to develop their business in the North East, and Cowans had found a site at Byker on the north of the Tyne. However Sheldon disagreed with this choice and eventually a site was located at Ravensthorpe near Dewsbury, in the triangle formed by the Calder Navigation Canal, the Leeds Dewsbury & Manchester Railway and the Lancashire & Yorkshire Railway. Regretfully problems with a mine-owner led to the negotiations breaking down and the partnership seemed doomed when Sheldon left to work in London for the marine engineers Maudslays. Cowans stayed on Tyneside, as one of Stephenson's managers, but the desire to establish his own business remained intact.

In 1842 and again in 1844, Cowans was invited to stay at the Bouch family home at Thursby near Carlisle. The purpose of these extended visits is not recorded, but it may have been to discuss the possibility of a joint business venture. In 1841 Bouch's younger brother, Thomas, 'discovered the ideal premises for a railway works' on the outskirts of Carlisle.

Whilst employed on the Lancaster & Carlisle Railway, he had been involved with the firm of Locke & Errington in purchasing some land belonging to the Woodbank Calico Works. The land required for that part of the L&CR belonged to one of the line's promoters, James Losh of Woodside House. Though Losh was an eminent judge, he is better known in historic circles as the man who introduced soda into this country. His family had interests in various railway ventures, and his brother George is remembered for the cast-iron locomotive wheel patent he shared with George Stephenson. The Losh holdings included a major stake in the Tyneside iron-works of Losh, Wilson and Bell, where George Dove, a close friend of Cowans, Sheldon and Bouch, was employed. Among Losh's other interests were the Woodbank Works that had been built by William Brummell in 1775, and during the mid-1840s they had passed into the ownership of Miss Sara Losh.

The lease on these works was apparently assigned to William Bouch in or around 1843-4, prior to his signing a formal lease in June 1846 when a local newspaper reported that 'the works had been taken over for the erection of a works for the manufacture of locomotive engines'.

There is no record as to the success of this venture, and it is virtually certain that no locomotives were ever manufactured at the site. Indeed, following his appointment as locomotive superintendent on the Stockton & Darlington Railway, Bouch was not able to carry on at Woodbank

There is some question as to why Bouch took on the venture when his appointment to the S&DR was imminent, unless it was part of a pre-arranged plan with his friends. In July 1846 Bouch wrote to Cowans saying he was prepared to assign the lease to him, and after an exchange of letters with Sheldon, the terms were agreed. In addition Cowans leased an adjacent farm, Woodbank House, from 8th August with the intention of working it to provide food. As the site was in a rural location, and some distance from Carlisle, he also negotiated the lease of several cottages from Sara Losh to house his workers. Other employees were later attracted from, or encouraged to settle in the nearby village of Upperby.

William Bouch

The choice of the Woodbank factory was clearly influenced by the fact that Carlisle was undoubtedly going to develop as a major railway centre in the coming years. A canal connected the city to the Solway Firth, and a railway linked it to Newcastle and the North East. Within a short period, new railways would also open to Maryport, Lancaster, and eventually Glasgow. Both men had connections with the city, as Cowans had been employed there during the building of the Newcastle & Carlisle Railway, whilst Sheldon held the unique distinction of being the first man to drive a locomotive into Carlisle when the line opened in 1838.

The money that Cowans and Sheldon had available was limited, so the Bouch brothers became involved in financing the partnership and this may well be what had been intended all along. Almost all of the equipment they owned at Woodbank (with a book value of no less than £725. 11s 9d), was transferred over to the partnership on 8th August 1846. In real terms, this was worth much more to Cowans, for if the new company had purchased the same second-hand equipment elsewhere it would have cost in excess of £1,200. Bouch put up a further £400 in cash, making a total of £1,125. 11s 9d, of which £125 was considered as a loan. Cowans and Sheldon each put up £500, giving the business a total working capital of £1,400.

Sarah Losh

With William and Thomas engaged on other projects, the Bouch brothers assumed the role of sleeping partners. Because their obligations took them all over the country, an arrangement was introduced whereby just one of them needed to be consulted over the business affairs of the firm, and they alternated in the role of 'sleeping partner' on an annual basis. From the outset we can see that all four partners had established contacts within the industry, and a fair amount of business was 'arranged' before the factory re-opened. The Woodbank lease was taken over on 1st September 1846 at an annual rent of £110. The estate covered over 33 acres, but the works themselves occupied only a small portion of the area.

Business began on 30th November, but it would appear that all the early work was a legacy left from Bouch's business including the first 20 forgings despatched to Gilkes, Wilson & Co, on 12th December. The company received the first 'new' order, for an engine crank pin (to a tracing from Shildon Engine Works), on 4th December. Between that date and the following March, twelve orders were received, nine of which had been commissioned by the Shildon works. This should hardly be surprising, when one considers William Bouch's position with the S&DR at the Shildon locomotive works. Additionally Bouch was also connected (through the S&DR) with Gilkes, Wilson & Co., and this Middlesborough-based firm paid Cowans, Sheldon over £500 in their first twelve months.

Thomas Bouch

In the next two years, business from these two sources increased even more, and the workforce expanded due to the greater demand for locomotive wheels. Cowans & Sheldon's first workforce was around ten foundry-men and boys. The average wage was 23 shillings (£1.15p) for a 60-hour week, paid fortnightly, two weeks in hand. The first pay bill seems to be one of £18 for the period ending 5th February 1847. Two weeks later the bill came to £22. 18s, and by the end of the year it was £42 per fortnight. In total, the wage bill for the first year came to £807 16s 6d (£45,000 at today's value) an average of £31 1s 5d per fortnight.

By August some 14 men and boys were employed, and as the work-force expanded all future staff recruitment was to be from the families of the employees at Woodbank.

For many years the firm was a 'closed shop', taking only apprentices from the sons of their workers.

Business was still being obtained from many of the railway companiess in which the Stephensons were involved as engineers or consultants, including the three railways that had by then reached Carlisle (from Lancaster, Maryport and Newcastle.

At first business was mostly for wagon and carriage wheels, axles and buffers, but the partners were actively pursuing other projects in an effort to extend its range. For a long time the firm's main business continued to be the engine wheel and crank pin work for the S&DR. However, after Thomas Bouch had completed his work on the L&C and was appointed as manager/engineer on the Edinburgh & Northern Railway, he influenced the placing of an order for the supply of 200 wagons with Cowans, Sheldon. Then, in August 1850 he arranged for 240 wagons to be supplied to the Edinburgh, Perth & Dundee Rly.

Orders for over £1,000 were placed by the Whitehaven & Furness Junction Railway, for various items including cattle creeps, wagon wheels, switches (points), and a variety of cast iron products. This was followed by more local contracts with the Kendal & Windermere, Cockermouth, Keswick & Penrith and the Cockermouth & Workington, railways. As the firm's reputation spread, new customers included the Lancashire & Yorkshire and the Sheffield, Ashton & Manchester railways.

Another first-time buyer was the Londonderry & Enniskillen Railway, who placed orders for loco crank axles, couplings and driving wheels in 1850. Later on this same concern were also to order locomotives from Cowans, Sheldon, who in turn arranged for these to be supplied by the London firm of William Bridges Adams The following March the first real export order was received from the Hamburg & Vegesock Railway.

By 1851, it was evident that the works were quickly being outgrown by the expanding business, which had diversified into supplying collieries and local ports with coal handling equipment. This diversification had come about, because the early railways were designed to carry coal from mines to the nearest port. Indeed, many railways either bought existing ports, purchased their own quays, or developed entirely new ports and harbours, that the railway and maritime industries became inextricably linked together - a position that would remain down the the nationalisation of transport in 1948, when docks and canals were given their own executive boards.

Inset: *View of Woodbank House, the small farm which John Cowans took over as his residence when he established his first 'locomotive' factory in the former calico works.*

Top Right: *The Newcastle & Carlisle Railway reaching Hexham, and at the celebratory event E.P. Sheldon drove the locomotive in to the town for Robert Stephenson. He was later to perform the same task when the railway reached Carlisle.* North of England Open Air Museum

Bottom Right: *Castings made at Woodbank were used in many famous railway construction projects, including some spectacular bridge projects. Here we see the South Durham & Lancashire Union Railway over Stainmore, with the construction of the famous Beulah Viaduct. The engineer on this project was none other than Thomas Bouch,*

Almost all the profit was ploughed back into the business as a means of extending the capital equipment, and financing work in progress. In 1851-2 the works were extended, and a water-powered tilt forge was constructed to draw water from the River Peterill. However, the most important asset was the siding that the L&CR had provided off the main line and into the works.

In 1851 Sheldon was travelling through London on an omnibus, when he was hit on the head by a stone, an incident that caused his gradual loss of sight and paralysis in his arm and leg. Even so he managed to continue a strong involvement with the business, though his activity as an engineer diminished. However, it was his skill as an administrator, which was now in demand as the company's forging work continued to increase - particularly in respect of wagon wheels and axles.

By 1852, it was evident that the Woodbank works could not handle all the business it was receiving, and it was consequently decided to transfer the forging side of the business to a new factory. As the majority of this work was coming from the North-east, the partners took a financial interest in the Darlington Forge Company who were in a number of ways offering products that were complimentary to those made at Cowans, Sheldon & Co.

By the following year all such work was transferred there. Sheldon took to visiting Darlington every week and another fine management team was soon established under his leadership. Despite the transfer of the forging business, the foundry work continued to grow dramatically. So much so, that within ten years of opening Woodbank, the partners were again faced with a decision to either form a third company or find new premises. With Sheldon being actively involved at Darlington, Cowans demanding work at Woodbank, and the Bouch brothers being otherwise occupied, there was not the managerial capacity to start yet another firm. Therefore, the only option was to find new premises, but nothing was immediately available in Carlisle!

S. SHELDON & Co Ltd.
CRANEMAKERS

THE MOVE TO ST NICHOLAS

In 1857 a bankrupt engineering works, on the site of the old St. Nicholas Leper Hospital, came on the market. Established by George Davy Richardson, the 1848 trade directory lists these works as being a foundry, saw mills and timber merchants. However, from the details contained in the Petition for Bankruptcy, it is evident that this firm were much more than that.

Details recorded at the Newcastle Sessions, seem to indicate that Richardson was involved in the manufacture of lifting equipment. Firstly: The works were sold with more cranes (as part of the fixtures and fittings), than could reasonably be expected to be found in a small engineering works. These included a steam powered 5-ton travelling crane on a carriage, a foundry crane, a single purchase winch, a wood crane, a 3-ton mobile crane, and finally four sets of sheer legs. Secondly: Most of the work in progress appeared to be related to crane-making, and two sets of 10-ton sheer legs, and one yard crane rated at 1$^{1}/_{2}$ tons were listed as 'nearing completion'.

Above: *Viewed around the mid-1920s, this view shows the St. Nicholas Works from the former Lancaster & Carlisle Railway, by this time part of the London, Midland & Scottish Railway's West Coast Main Line.*

As the St. Nicholas Works were only a few years old, they were constructed in 'a most substantial manner, and equipped with the most modern machinery available.' Much of this machinery reflects a capacity to manufacture cranes; including lathes of 48" and 24" face diameter, spike machines, a six-foot boring bar, large grind wheels, and a [sic] waggon-wheel pressing machine in the fitting shop. The saw mill was fitted with a 30-foot double circular saw, a smaller similar machine, an upright turning machine, boring machines, and 40 circular saws with diameters ranging from 12" to 48". The foundry was similarly well equipped, whilst the works had an excellent outside area, complete with stables, a lorry and two timber carts (all of which were horse-drawn).

All the equipment on the site was worked by 12 or 13 horsepower stationary steam-engines, with a small boiler house located alongside the foundry. Internal railway sidings were provided with a connection to the N&CR, which in turn communicated with the LNWR (L&CR) line, and those to Maryport, West Cumbria, Silloth Bay and Port Carlisle. Strategically, the works could not have been in a better place for the development of a new 'railway' engineering works.

The works were sold to Cowans, Sheldon at a public auction on Tuesday 14th July 1857, and details of the proceedings were reported in the local paper: 'The sale of Mr. Richardson's works at St. Nicholas was conducted on Tuesday last, by Mr. William Browne on behalf of Geo. Davy Richardson's creditors and assignees. Selling the works and all moveable plant, machinery and apparatus, the auction began at 12 O'clock in the forenoon, whereupon all the buildings and contents were offered in a single lot, though it was presumed that there would be want of a buyer for the whole establishment, spirited bidding began in earnest. Several gentlemen from Newcastle, the West of Cumberland, and Carlisle were in attendance, and bidding was begun by a gentleman from Jesmond upon Tyne at the sum of £1,200.

After bidding remained stationary at £1,500 the price was run up to £2,500. Upon Mr. Browne declaring a sale at £2,500, the bidding became more spirited, and after a severe contest the premises including all heavy fixed machinery and raw materials were finally knocked down to Messrs Cowans, Sheldon & Company of Woodbank for £3,100.'

Included in the sale price (which would be about £250,000 at today's value) were 14,000 feet of hardwood timber in planks of $1^1/_2$ to $3^1/_2$ inches in thickness, and several thousand feet of large grown round-wood in oak, ash and other timbers. All the steel stock and wrought and cast iron were included in the sale. There was a separate auction for hand tools and small stores, but Cowans, Sheldon's agent was unable to secure these lots in their entirety, and many of the items were sold to private individuals. Of most value were the numerous foundry patterns, which the records show included items that had been supplied to the N&CR, M&CR, L&CR and several other railways.

Below: *A standard turntable in the 40- to 45-ft dia. range and of the type supplied to the North British, Caledonian, Midland and LMS railways. This 42-ft table went to the Clyde Trustees in 1932.*

Exactly what Richardson had supplied to these railways has not been revealed despite extensive research, but I feel confident in saying that parts were manufactured for both wagon and coach construction. Other information fuels the speculation, that this was the first firm to manufacture railway cranes in Carlisle.

The acquisition of St. Nicholas did not resolve all the problems facing the partners, for their managerial capacity was stretched to its limit. Due to the worsening condition of his eyes, Sheldon was finding it increasingly difficult to manage his responsibilities. Operating on three sites highlighted this dramatically, even though by this time the Darlington Forge had become almost self-managing.

As there was no one available from within the company their old friend, George Dove was brought in as manager of the new works on the basis that he would eventually become an equal partner. Sheldon took over the company books and Dove took on the day-to-day running of the works.

Above: *This steam-travelling crane with tripod-legs was one of the firm's earliest steam crane productions - possibly Carlisle & Silloth Bay Dock, Harbour & Railway Co.'s No. 4 ordered in December 1856 and delivered the following September.*

The partners made Dove a more than a generous offer to him under a partnership deed in 1858 and he became a full partner in 1863. The deed showing the changes in the firm has proved to be very useful in my research, but it is far too complex a document to record here. However, it serves as a record of the success enjoyed by the original partnership.

From 1846 they had gone from a cash position of around £1,400 with fixtures and fittings of £700, to one of £13,737 8s 6d. This figure was comprised of £3,721 0s 0d for Land, Workshops and Buildings, £5,834 6s 7d for plant and machinery, and book debts or cash to the value of £4,182 1s 11d. This did not include a profit of £1,576 6s 10d which had been carried over to the General Profit & Loss Account.

All of this was remarkably achieved in a period of less than twelve years. But better results would follow, as the business became more specific under Dove. In time he introduced a new order number system as the main manufacturing capacity was transferred to the new works. The firm declined to accept miscellaneous manufacturing orders, and existing contracts for 'small items' were continued at Woodbank in the old order book. Dove began to concentrate on more specialised products, though exactly when he began building cranes is not clearly defined. However, an early St. Nicholas works order (number 31) was for a 'Crane Pillar to turn, same as number 32 Crane' supplied to Darlington Forge.

If the theory of Richardson's being crane-makers is to be accepted, then it follows that such work would have been added to the Cowans Sheldon range after the acquisition of the St. Nicholas works. That first crane was supplied on 5th August 1858, but it was not until December the following year that the first railway crane rolled out of the works behind a Maryport & Carlisle shunter. That was order number 45, a 2½-ton hand travelling crane purchased by Oldham Corporation.

Dove obviously saw the potential for developing the crane business, but he was also keen to expand into other fields. Around 1859 Cowans began developing a range of wooden wagon turntables for use in goods yards and warehouses, where space was insufficient for rail turnouts. From such humble origins, the company soon became established as world-beating manufacturers of locomotive, carriage, and wagon turntables.

In the 15 years that followed, a staggering total of 532 turntables were produced - all were between 12- and 45-feet in diameter. The exception was a nine-foot diameter turntable supplied to the Whitehaven Junction Railway in 1860, but the most common size was 42-feet. Orders were not limited to the home market, for by now they were exporting to Russia, India, Australia, Egypt and Denmark.

Cowans Sheldon had been the first to make turntables on the 'balance-on-centre' principle, abolishing the need for the use of the time-consuming geared winches previously considered as an integral part of all such products. Water cranes, parachute tanks and standard water columns were also a considerable part of the foundry's business, with drawing No. 23 (8" cast iron water column) being used by at least 14 separate companies as their standard type. In all 300 pieces of locomotive watering equipment were supplied between 1865 and 1872. Though the trade in cranes was increasing, the capacities were hardly impressive, with the average maximum capacity being around 2½-tons. During 1859-60 only nine 5-ton cranes were made, but in 1861 a few 10-ton travelling cranes were built for stock. This was an unusual move for the firm who rarely made anything for stock throughout their entire history.

Top Right: *The Redheugh Bridge across the Tyne, designed by Thomas Bouch, which contained many castings supplied by Cowans Sheldon to Gilkes Wilson.*

Bottom Right: *A typical Cowans Sheldon water crane, this one being an 8" model to drawing No.23.*

In February 1863 the Glasgow & Paisley Railway ordered a 15-ton yard crane, but delivery on this was deferred until November. As capacities and sizes increased the Inverness & Aberdeen Railway ordered a 20-ton overhead crane, whilst a similar 25-ton crane was built for internal use at the St. Nicholas works. Cowans probably made another overhead crane for stock, because when the North Eastern Railway ordered a 30-ton model in December 1864 it was supplied within a month. Export crane orders started around 1865, with a major contract being placed by the Great Indian Peninsular Railway Co., for two 10-ton steam travelling cranes and four 5-ton travelling cranes.

The first steam station crane, rated at 10-tons, was supplied to the NER in August 1867. It seems as though steam-powered machinery developed under Dove, and a new boiler-making shop was constructed in 1860-1. Previous to this, boilers for steam powered machinery had been ordered from Hawks & Co of Gateshead. The construction of steam engines at Carlisle began about 1862, with these being made to a variety of designs. However, it seems as though the majority were built for coupling to steam cranes. The first known steam engine is No. 16, a pair of 14" cylinder vertical engines for use in the works. Those that followed varied in cylinder size from $6^1/_2$" to 15", with the stroke varying from 10" to 2-foot. Boilers were both to horizontal and vertical patterns. Customers during this period were the Gt. Indian Peninsular Rly, Darlington Forge, and Britannia Iron Co., though the largest engine was one with a 30" cylinder supplied to the Consett Iron Works. By the end of the partnership, some 84 steam engines had been supplied or were under construction.

The partners managed to pay themselves a handsome dividend every year, as the profits never fell below $22^1/_2$%. This benefited Dove, for in addition to his salary, his share of the profits went to pay for his full share in the partnership. Likewise, the business continued to prosper and generous sums were put back in to help development. Dove and Cowans were always wanting new equipment, but the ever-cautious Sheldon kept a tight check on the money, and managed to beat down his suppliers' price on almost every occasion. For example in 1861 his statement showed that only £911 19s 8d had been spent on Machinery and Tools, in which were included two lathes, one planning machine and a slotting machine. In 1868 his report, he showed that he had spent the sum of £949 9s 5d, which included a new radial drill, plate planing and wheel moulding machinery, a new slide rest for the large lathe, and extensions for the two overhead cranes.

Above: *Typical of the warehouse cranes being built by Cowans Sheldon in the 1860s-70s, is the 5-ton hand-operated crane constructed for the North Eastern Railway. Around 35 such cranes were delivered in the period concerned, and this is one supplied to York.*

Below: *A low-capacity hand-operated breakdown crane of the 1870s seen long after its railway life is over. This example has found use as a dockside crane alongside the River Nile. It was still at work in 1972, its centenary year, but its oil drum support looks hardly secure!* Walter Campsie

THE LIMITED COMPANY

By 1869 Cowans was becoming very ill, and though only in his mid-50s, he was forced to take on less work. Accordingly, at the partnership's annual meeting in 1869, the decision was taken to surrender the lease for Woodbank. The transfer of the remaining machinery and business took almost a full year, being completed on 16th July 1870. This date is almost coincidental with that of Cowans' retirement, and his move of home from Woodbank House to the South of England. However not all the equipment was transferred to St. Nicholas, for a considerable amount went to other businesses in which the partners had an interest. For example, the tilt forge was transferred to an enterprise partly owned by Cowans and Miss Ann Bouch, namely the Dalston Forge Co., located a few miles south-west of Carlisle. Cowans premature retirement was very short, and he passed away in 1873 at Cranford, Middlesex.

Above: *An interior view of the St. Nicholas works foundry c1924. The miscellany of the foundryman's trade is seen; wooden patterns, casting blocks, casting sand, ladles, small molds and shovels.*

There then followed a considerable period of acrimony, as Cowan's nominees began litigation with the company. This cast a shadow over the future of the business at a time when Sheldon was also in ill health and the Bouch brothers were advancing in years.

As a result Mrs. Cowans suggested selling the firm, but as no buyer was found the idea was dismissed and it was decided to reform the partnership. However, as it seemed likely that none of the three remaining original partners would make old bones, a decision was taken to create a limited liability company, with Dove as Managing Director and Sheldon as Financial Director.

Above: *The demise of Thomas Bouch can be clearly attributed to the aftermath of the Tay Bridge Disaster, which occurred on 31st December 1879 and claimed at least 70 lives. Bouch had been proclaimed a hero when he first spanned the Forth of Tay (our picture shows the bridge being constructed), but vilified when it collapsed. A study of the subject shows that Bouch was made into a scapegoat on to whom all the blame could be heaped. His death in 1880 robbed Cowans Sheldon of the expertise of one of Britain's most eminent railway engineers of his time. Dundee City Libraries*

Left: *This early breakdown crane, on the South Eastern & Chatham Railway is seen at Longhedge Engine Shed (east of Clapham Junction) in or around 1895. It features a Cowans Sheldon crane in the formation. The crane is works order No. 1013 supplied in 1880, and is built on a 6-wheel underframe. Peter Tatlow collection.*

The prospectus was for a nominal capital of £60,000 in 200 £300 shares, but this was amended twice before the firm was incorporated on 28th March 1873. The 600 new shares, each worth £100, were issued to Dove, Sheldon, William and Thomas Bouch, and the nominees of John Cowans. The same arrangement occurred at Darlington Forge, with that company being formed of 770 £100 shares. William Putnam the Managing Director was awarded 140 shares, with 630 share being divided into three equal portions between the Bouch family, Cowans-nominees, and E.P. Sheldon.

Even so this did not appear to satisfy Cowans' family, and for several years the rumblings continued, until the company eventually bought back each of their 210 shares at £44 each. Yet even this huge sum of over £9,000 did not stifle the acrimony, as the family felt that they were worth twice that and there were repeated claims for money. Naturally this period of change was an anxious time for all the employees at St. Nicholas, and Sheldon handed over the company books to his assistant William G. Watt.

Watt was made the Company Secretary on a salary of £250 per annum, with an additional 2% of the net divisible profits. Sheldon now took things more leisurely and maintained only a passing interest in the business, a circumstance dictated by his failing sight and ill health. As a consequence Dove was forced to spend more time in senior management and less time in the works,. His assistant John Horne was appointed as the new Works Manager on a salary of £200, and offered the same profit sharing scheme as W.G. Watt.

At the firm's third Quarterly Meeting in 1873, Thomas Wright was appointed as a Director and given the task of supervising the work's improvement programme. This commenced with the first building - a small boiler-testing shop that came into use on 24th July 1874. On 1st January 1875 a new stable block, a new fitting shop, a turntable shop and a large machine shop came into use, but still more facilities were to follow. including a 20-ton weigh-machine near the entrance gate. It was erected on a plot of land by the railway siding, and came into use in December 1876. Two more fitting shops were completed in 1877, the principle of these being 204-ft long by 90-ft wide, with an internal minimum height of 90-ft. Because the capacity of the foundry was being continually out-grown, this part of the factory became a bottleneck in the production programme.

Top Right: *Quite what this item of heavy equipment actually is, is open to question. The order book of June 1892 gives no clue to its identity other than stating 'double winder to special order' and no customer is identified.*

Bottom Right: *Coaling equipment was produced at both the Woodbank and St. Nicholas Works, but it has been difficult to find any views of this equipment in its original form. Despite its poor quality, this view of an NER 0-6-0 (No 1191) at Waskerley Depot on the Stanhope & Tyne Railroad is representative of an early piece of coaling equipment.*

Above: *In 1879 the firm invested in a new belt-drive system to power machinery in the works from a central power source. It is seen here in 1937, still working well 60 years later.*

Extensions were then put in hand, and a new foundry measuring 332 by 81 feet with two new cupolas was brought into use in the autumn of 1877. There was also heavy investment in new machinery, including two 15-ton overhead steam cranes for internal use. In the blacksmiths shop two new steam hammers and a fan-blast were installed, whilst the boiler shop got a new steam riveter. To celebrate these events and the 30th anniversary of the firm, an outing was arranged to Keswick on 10th August 1877. A train for 250 people was chartered, and the work force, their families, and the Directors were accompanied by a brass band.

Boiler-making did not expand under the new management, and only 44 boilers were made between 1873 and 1881. However, if the number was not of interest, then the diversity was; egg-shaped, cylindrical, horizontal, vertical, plain-ended and creosote receivers all being produced for British customers. On the other hand, heavy lifting equipment became another area in which the firm began to specialise following an order from the North East Marine Engineering Co. in 1879. The order for a set of 30-ton steam sheer legs was placed in 1881, along with orders for five single sheet overhead cranes rated between 10- and 60-tons. This was the start of the expansion into heavy marine and dock cranes, which eventually involved a considerable degree of business with the Admiralty.

One new area of business was the manufacture of traversers, with types for locomotives, carriages and railway wagons. The biggest orders for traversers came from 'down-under', with the New Zealand Government Railways being a major customer. Yet this period was not a happy one for the firm, even though it weathered the economic depression of 1879-1881. The problem was compounded by the fact that investment in British railways dropped to an all-time low, and the world scene was only slightly better.

Thomas Wright died in 1878, and it was decided to leave his place on the board vacant, at least whilst the litigation with the Cowans-nominees was continuing. Because of the ill-feeling that arose at this time, there were several proposals to drop the name of Cowans from the business but on each occasion the vote was narrowly defeated. The name Cowans Sheldon had become well-established world-wide by then, and it was feared a change might affect public confidence. So Cowans' name remained, which in many ways is ironic, because following the amalgamation into the NEI group, it was the name of Sheldon that disappeared when the firm became NEI-Cowans Boyd.

Above: *An example of the breakdown cranes being made for the home market at the turn of the century is seen in the recovery of a Great Central Railway 0-6-2T.*

Below: *An overseas example from the same period is this 30-ton crane for South African Railways.*

In the eight years following the formation of the limited liability company, all the original partners passed away and the entire management of the company rested on the shoulders of George Dove. Thomas Bouch' son (William junior) commenced his first term of office in April 1881 and took the Bouch family's position on the board; he was to remain an enthusiastic and active Director until his death. Just a few weeks later E.P. Sheldon passed away, dying quietly at his Carlisle home on 15th May. Thus leaving another seat on the board vacant, and the company without a Chairman. This was resolved at the annual general meeting on 24th August, when Sheldon's younger brother John was appointed.

The annual report for the year ending June 1881 stated:- 'In the removal by death of Sir Thomas Bouch and Mr. E.P. Sheldon, the company has sustained an irreparable loss. Although engaged in other and more important duties, the former was ever ready by counsel to aid in developing the business, while Mr. Sheldon by his rare combination of mechanical and financial ability, and his unceasing interest and attention, most materially helped to establish and sustain the reputation of the firm.'

In 1886, whilst preparing legal documents in connection with the acquisition of some additional land for the installation of a £3,000 hydraulic plant, the firm's bankers found that a major error had been made by solicitors during the formation of the limited company, and they had to apply to the High Court for this error to be corrected.

Thereafter the Directors of each company were not to number less than three or more than six, and each Director had to have a holding of not less than £250. Accordingly, on 31st May/1st June 1887, the 752 original shares were surrendered and new shares issued as follows: George Dove senior, 317: George Dove junior, 7: John Charles Dove, 5: William G. Watt, 8: John Horne, 6: the executors of E.P. Sheldon, 322: the executors of Sir Thomas Bouch, 164: Miss Ann Bouch, 164: and the executors of Thomas Wright, 7. Other share-dealings worth recording, are those instances where the firm took holdings in railway ventures in lieu of payment (presumably because of bad debts). At the AGM of September 1882, it was reported that the value of the firm's shareholdings had declined in two cases and it was proposed that the shares in the Solway Junction and Tottenham & Hampstead Junction railways, should 'be sold without any delay or hindrance'.

Top Left: *It has emerged that some small pattern work was carried on at Woodbank long after the move to St. Nicholas, and the Cowans family retained an interest in the dairy farm at Woodbank House.*

Bottom Left: *A view of the erecting shop in 1903 with what is described as a 'double-drum slip winding engine built for the North Eastern Marine Engineering Co.* Michael T L Dove

At the same time it was reported that shares had been 'bought' in lieu of debt for the Londonderry & Loughswilly Railway in the rural west of Ireland, a venture which hardly promised to make massive returns. One of the larger 'debts into shares' transactions was noted in 1885, when the firm were then forced to take bonds in the Maryport Harbour for a judgement of £2,042 19s 11d.

Following the death of John Sheldon in 1889, his son John George Sheldon took his seat on the board in June 1890 and William Bouch Jnr. was appointed Chairman. The Sheldon shares had passed on to the nephews and nieces of E.P. Sheldon who had no children of his own. Regretfully this led to yet another argument, for two of the new shareholders immediately sought to sell their interests.

Even so, according to the firm's articles of association, they were not allowed to do this for two years, and so they tried to sell them. It was directly against the firm's policy to do this, so it led to another lengthy period of litigation, but on this occasion the company won, and the dissenting parties were forced to hold on to their shares for three years. Interestingly, John Cowans junior purchased 15 of these £100 shares, presumably the earlier rifts between the family and the firm had finally been healed.

The period ending 1891 was one of steady, if not spectacular progress. Primarily the main orders still came from British railway companies, and there were no less than 31 separate companies on their books. However, railway expansion was slowly coming to an end in Britain, with only a small proportion of the country's eventual network as then not built. Consequently, the firm concentrated on developing its overseas business, and expanding into marine and naval lifting equipment. Having achieved a degree of stability, the firm maintained a dividend of over 5% every year. Fortunately it also continued the use of profits to build a reserve fund, which was of considerable benefit in years to come.

In 1882 and 1897 production was badly affected by strikes, due to national wage disputes, even though labour-relations at the firm were usually of the highest order. From 1882 to 1892, the firm held a balanced turnover, which varied between £40,000 and £50,000 per annum, and a nominal sum of £5,000 was carried over each year. Orders to hand varied between £16,000 and £25,000 throughout the same period, and at any given time there was normally at least four to six months work. Though in an outwardly healthy position, the business was in fact not as dynamic as it could have been, possibly due to the fact that George Dove was growing old.

His son, John Charles Dove, had been appointed as a Director in 1888. Despite the fact that he was an engineer of considerable talent, he was not of the same calibre as his father. As a consequence, most of the work now fell upon the two other Directors, John Horne, and the new Company Secretary James Walter Brown. Output from Cowans Sheldon continued steadily from 1890 onwards, with almost 800 turntables and 600 cranes being produced in the last decade of the 19th century.

Most of the work at this time came due to the demand for larger products, as locomotives and freight loads increased in size. However, railways were slow to replace an installation once it was in position, and some went to unusual lengths to increase the capacity of earlier models. During the period 1885-1905 the company received a host of turntable-extension orders, but it would appear that they were only accepted with great reluctance. Though it was feasible to extend a turntable's diameter by anything up to nine feet, the resulting structure was neither durable nor completely stable, and when in use these extensions manifested numerous 'problems'.

Problems with regard to reliability were especially experienced by the North British Railway at St. Margaret's (Edinburgh), where the extended turntable was prone to breakdowns and it eventually had to be replaced with a brand new one. Interestingly, the repairs cost the NBR more than they actually paid to install the new turntable. Naturally a lot of correspondence followed, with each side blaming one another, but it was a case of putting new wine in old wine skins!

Cranes were another matter, for as average weight-loads increased, the conventional 25-cwt hand cranes installed in goods depots, yards and warehouses were worse than useless. Many of these had been supplied in the period from 1846 to 1870 and even those cranes rated at up to $2^1/2$ tons were barely sufficient for modern demands. This resulted in 3-ton and 5-ton models becoming the more standard range, but the number of models in the 10-ton to 20-ton capacities was also increasing.

Some work was undertaken to up-rate the early-model cranes, but it was mainly new cranes that were being supplied for breakdown and accident duties, as locomotives, wagons, and coaches all increased in size and weight. The same sort of progress was evidenced in marine, dock and harbour crane orders. As the switch from sail to steam became more progressive as the 19th century went on, newer, bigger merchant vessels were plying the seas. To cater for this traffic, the various ports were provided with bigger, more powerful cranes, hoists and winches by Cowans Sheldon.

The biggest demands came for coaling cranes, and through the 1880s and 1890s, the company had a very full order book for this type of product. During the 1890s they expanded their range of hydraulic products, and applied this 'new' technology to cranes, capstans and turntables. The process was not actually all that new, for Sir W.G. Armstrong & Co. had made hydraulic lifting equipment at their Elswick (Newcastle) works as early as 1847. Indeed Cowans Sheldon had even made some hydraulic equipment for the NER under licence from Armstrong's.

Right: *Shunting on the internal railway at the St. Nicholas Works was rarely done by locomotive, and Cowans Sheldon had no locomotive of their own. When a locomotive was needed, one was usually loaned from one of the city's engine sheds, normally that at Upperby. Otherwise all internal movement was done by using one of the factory's travelling cranes that ran along broad gauge tracks. At different periods up to four travelling cranes might be used in the works at a time.*
This December 1939 view shows the works crane moving amongst a forest of crane jibs and components awaiting completion. On the opposite side of St. Nicholas Bridge, two much earlier sheer leg cranes can be seen in the yard of Hewitson's slate works. By this time a portion of this yard had been taken over as a war salvage dump, and large quantities of scrap (including a traction engine) can just be made out.

Above: *A 1902 view of the offices, where no less than 45 drawing tables with their integral drawing/chart drawers were located.*

Below: *Steelwork being erected at Carlisle Market Hall; was this the greatest railway station that never held a train?*

Cowans first recorded 'hydraulic' order was received in 1873, when three 1-ton ingot presses were supplied to the West Cumberland Iron Co. The first hydraulic turntable seems to have been supplied to drawing no. 4282, which called for two 50-ft engine turntables for the NER in 1875, with delivery in May the following year. An interesting diversion in the company's product range came in the 1890s, when Carlisle City Council experienced trouble with the contractors for the new Market Hall. Having been badly let down with the steelwork for the roof, George Dove arranged to take over, and the fine ironwork they installed emains to this day. There can be little doubt that the company's involvement was not altogether without some form of altruism, and the ironwork may well have been seen as part of a strategy to gain further business.

If you stand in Carlisle Market Hall today, you will not fail to gain the impression that this is less a civic building and more a railway station. When viewed from above, the bay-like structure of the roof is not dissimilar to contemporary station buildings of that time period. It should be remembered that the railways were then commissioning fine station buildings to reflect their financial solidarity - which was absolutely essential to encourage investment in Victorian times. These were the stable things in which investors liked to place their money, not in locomotives, rolling stock and similar items that would depreciate rather than grow in value.

References in the Cowans Sheldon records would appear to indicate that this building was to be a showpiece, a real-life example of the type of structural steelwork that the company could produce for its railway customers. Furthermore there are several examples of agents of colonial railways being taken to view the Market Hall after it opened, and we may assume that these representatives were not going to buy half a dozen eggs or a couple of cabbages. Whatever the case, Carlisle got a fine market hall, the city fathers shaved a few pounds off the price and Cowans probably got a little bit of business on the side.

Friendships, handshakes and keeping it in the town were considered quite laudable practices back then in the good old days! However, as the management structure of the company had changed considerably, Dove recognised that the personal friendships on which Cowans Sheldon & Co. had been established would not sustain the company into the next century. Therefore, in 1893 it was thought desirable to change the Articles of Association. Even so, the period 1892-5 was a bad time for heavy engineering generally, as a severe economic depression affected the entire country.

At the time Cowans Sheldon had a good order book, though the majority of orders came from India, the North East Marine Engineering and the NER. Even so the firm began to take orders from the Admiralty that were quite unusual, including several 2-ton hydraulic tobacco presses and sugar cane crushers for the Royal Navy Caribbean Rum Plant.

In 1893 things tightened a little and the company reduced prices to gain orders, and managed to win several orders from the Manchester, Sheffield & Lincolnshire Railway, which they had quoted for at a higher price in 1891. The year 1894 was quite bad for the firm, and they started making items for stock, though these were somehow (and quite fortuitously) sold before the work was actually completed.

Despite this apparently unfavourable climate, the company decided to put large sums from the 'reserve account' into an expansion programme. All the adjoining land that the directors could get hold of was purchased, and new workshops were added.

The works were then comprised of the commercial offices, a large drawing office, extensive structural shops, iron and brass foundries, machine shops, forging shops, numerous stores, a joinery works, and two large fitting and erecting shops. The whole plant being linked up with a variety of internal railway tracks of differing gauges. Dove also insisted on installing the best, most modern types of machinery and equipment, and spent over £36,000 in the two years after the death of E.P. Sheldon. There can be little doubt for the need of the items purchased, and perhaps some things were long over due, but such extravagance would not have suited Sheldon's cautious nature. By 1903, over £70,000 from the profits had been ploughed back into new equipment.

Below: *Although taken in 1948, this picture shows the overhead travelling crane installed in 1902. Electrically powered, it had a capacity to lift 20-tons. Two further 10-ton cranes, installed at the same time, are seen at the opposite end of the workshop.*

LOAD NOT TO EXCEED 20 TON

Such investment led to the works being furnished with some of the most up to date equipment in the world. There were lathes of various sizes and machines for planing, boring, slotting, punching, shaping, milling and screwing. A variety of drills performed work that had formerly been done by hammer and chisel or file. Most of the machinery was belt driven, and powered by a large engine at one end of the fitting shop. It worked steadily and noiselessly away at the rate of 60 strokes a minute and a numbering machine on its side recorded that the machinery was going at the proper speed.

A Naysmith steam hammer was used to accomplish the essential forging work, which had now become an integral part of crane making. The forge was equipped with several cupolas, and huge hydraulic presses were installed to handle sheet steel up to $1^{1}/_{2}$ inches thick. A hydraulic rivet press was also installed in the same shop, and with simplicity of action it performed the previously noisy task with silent efficiency. A huge circular saw was employed to cut through great bars of iron and steel, and it handled the task as though it was slicing timber. An automatic saw sharpener stood alongside, and worked quietly away all the time, sharpening a tooth at a time, so that by the time one circular saw blade was blunt, another was ready to take its place.

The offices had also seen much improvement by the time the firm reached its 50th anniversary. To give an idea of how large it had become, an excellent article in the *Carlisle Express* gave a report of the business. Much of that has been used for the information contained in this chapter, but its description of the offices are worthy of quoting verbatim:-

'If you go into Mr. Dove's private office you will see suspended upon the wall a map of India, showing all the Indian Railways, and there is not some railway laid upon that map, which has not been supplied by this firm with some of their specialities, those specialities comprising engine turntables, steam and hydraulic cranes, "breakdown" cranes, watering tanks, masting sheers, and half-a-dozen other contrivances for facilitating the work in goods yards, engine sheds, railway stations and docks. There are photographs of these appliances all around the room, besides pictures of the Carlisle Market roof, and before we go outside into the works it is worthwhile to look at Mr. Dove's gallery of portraits. There at the top is Mr. Losh, there are Robert Stephenson, two of the Hawthornes (with whom Mr. Dove was a pupil). William Bouch of the Stockton & Darlington Railway, and a few other mechanical engineers of the Tyneside District for which Mr. Dove always has a "soft side".'

Left: *The links between Cowans Sheldon and Tyneside were very strong. At the mouth of the River Tyne this huge Titan crane was established at the North Pier in 1903 It travelled on its own track, and spanned a temporary railway siding that ran alongside.*

Right: *These two views of the Lancashire & Yorkshire Railway's 40-ton electric coaling crane at Goole Docks are of great interest, as they show how coal was laboriously transferred from railway wagons to coasting colliers. Picking up just one wagon at a time, the crane lifts it up on a cradle from the quayside siding, and swings it round to a position above the ship's (SS Westerdale) hold. When it was in position, one end of the wagon would be lowered 45 degrees, and the coal would discharge by gravity through an 'end-tipping' door in the 20-ton L&YR wagon.*

Business picked up in 1896, but during the latter part of that year the works were affected by a dispute between the Amalgamated Engineers' Union, and the engineering employers. This was a direct result of the recession a few years earlier, and the union's conviction that the recent difficulties, and future prosperity, were bound up with a reduction in working hours.

A magical 8-hour day was the goal, and a six-month long strike ensued - seriously affecting both the union and the employers. On resumption of normal working, the company began earning profits in excess of £10,000 annually. This led to a resumption of the 'postponed' works-improvement scheme, which had commenced with the installation of new 'Lancashire' boilers, and a dynamo house with 110 volts output.

Electrical power was to provide Dove (and his fellow Directors) with the impetus to move forward into a new century with new technology. Electrically-powered equipment was a field into which the firm quickly moved, but the first 'experiments' were items for their own works. The 30-ton overhead crane was converted from steam to electric drive in May 1897, and a similar crane being built for the new fitting shop was also given electric motors.

This may not seem to be anything of consequence in today's high-powered micro-chip and push-button world, but in the last years of Queen Victoria it was light-years ahead. Cowans were quick to point out the advantages to their customers, and the first order for electrically driven equipment came in October 1897, with three 5-ton overhead cranes for the East Indian Railway.

The first electrically driven turntable appears to be one of 16-ft diameter supplied to Harland & Wolff in 1898, whilst the following year, the Glasgow & South Western Railway ordered the first electric traverser. However, this new technology reduced the profits, as the work became even more labour intensive. In the first five years of the 20th century, profits and dividend were reduced by half, except for 1902, which was a particularly good year. This was the year in which the L&YR ordered a 20-ton steam accident crane and placed an enquiry for a 40-ton steam Goliath crane.

INTO THE 20TH CENTURY

In 1903 the NER ordered a series of cranes for use on their docks at Middlesborough and Hartlepool, but by far the biggest customer that year was the Admiralty. The following two years were lean times for the firm, and the orders for the period do not even fill a double page in the works order book. What little work to be found was mainly from docks and dockyards. Throughout the railway industry times were hard, for the main period of expansion was over. The last major rail project in Britain - the GCR's London Extension, had been good business for Cowans Sheldon, who supplied cranes, loco hoists, wheel drops, water columns, fairleads, capstans and turntables, but those days were now just a memory.

In 1906 George Dove sadly died, and following his death the firm floundered like a leaky boat in a raging sea. John Charles Dove did little to stem the flow, and in the next two years the firm only secured 76 crane orders. Finally, in 1907, a significant development took place that captured J. C. Dove's imagination as the first floating crane was constructed at St. Nicholas. These had been pioneered in Germany in the early years of the century, and there is no doubt that an order for a 150-ton floating crane for the China & Japan Trading Co. helped the firm through this bad period. The years of 1909-10 showed no major improvement, as the firm only supplied nine orders for railway cranes in that period.

Left: *This 60-ton travelling crane was ordered by the War Office in December 1914. No indication is given as to the delivery point, but it is thought to have been the munitions works at Gretna.*

Inset: *Brigadier General Sir John Stevens Cowans 1862-1921, who joined the British Army in 1882 and rose to Quarter-Master General during World War I.*

Two of these orders are of interest: the first of these was a $1^3/_4$-ton Double Track Transporter for the L&YR at Fleetwood. Also in 1909, the second steam-accident crane was built for the Taff Vale Rly; but at 35-tons it was one of the largest of its type thus far manufactured in Carlisle. In 1910 only four turntable orders were placed, completing a disastrous decade in which there were (on average) just 18 orders a year for turntable products. The period did witness an increase in size if not volume, and the first 70-ft diameter table was constructed to order no. 2640 for the Caledonian Railway in 1903.

Turntables of 60-ft diameter had become commonplace during the decade, and examples were supplied to the North Eastern, Caledonian, Great Central, Glasgow & South Western, Callander & Oban, London & North Western, North British and two foreign railways. The Midland had been the first to set the trend for 60-ft dia. turntables, when No. 2442 was supplied to Saltley in 1899. This increasing of capacities was echoed in every field of the company's activity, except water cranes, where 6 to 8 inch columns remained the norm.

Up to the outbreak of war in 1914, the firm concentrated on heavier lifting equipment and larger turntables. Even so the older style of hand cranes were still being ordered by the railway companies, as evidenced by no. 3298 a 5-ton hand breakdown crane supplied to the Metropolitan Railway in 1913.

Profit was at an all time low before the war, with only a 5% dividend paid in 1912 and none at all in the following two years. The reason quoted in Dove's report was "owing to the amount of work in progress upon which the profit or loss is undetermined". These were expansionist years, and the company was failing to capitalise on them, and one can only assume deficiencies in the management as the root cause. That a steadying influence was necessary was evident enough, but the problem was one of convincing the Directors.

Pressure was brought to bear by John Cowans' eldest son, Brigadier General John Cowans who, disappointed at the lack of the dividend, presented 'forcible arguments'. Consequently, early in 1914 John Barrington Pearson the Principal Outdoor Machinery Superintendent at the NER's Darlington works was appointed as the new general manager. He knew the firm well, having been a regular visitor to the works in order to inspect work-in-progress. It is a mark of his capability, that his meteoric progress at Darlington was achieved before his 30th birthday. Though the order book seemed healthy on his appointment, the profitability was very poor. However, he had barely got his feet under the table when war was declared, and he requested that he be released for war service. This was alarming news, and the request was refused on the grounds that 'he was of more benefit to the country if he stayed home and sorted out the works for increased war capacity.'

The firm saw a diversity of orders, with work arriving from the Admiralty, Ministry of Munitions, the Russian Ministry, Messrs Vickers and Sir W. G. Armstrong & Co. In October 1915, the Directors were asked to release Mr. Pearson and allow him to take over duties as Assistant Superintendent of the Royal Laboratory, Woolwich Arsenal. As the request was influenced by General Cowans the Directors took little time in considering. Meanwhile Cowans had already distinguished himself by his efficiency and remained ever unperturbed at the enormous task of overseeing the huge expansion of Britain's army services during the war years.

In December Pearson left for Woolwich and Mr. E. Boynton, was appointed as Acting-Manager. Other employees were released for war service, and each married man serving in HM forces had a 5-shilling weekly allowance paid to their wives. That the war was a profitable time, is clearly seen by the annual dividend of 10%, which was maintained throughout the duration.

In 1918 Pearson (by then a Director of the company) returned to Carlisle, and took over the entire operation once more. He took the order books and completely re-organised them, and from 1919 onwards, cranes, turntables, water cranes, traversers, and winches were no longer given a separate order number series; partially because the business was changing as the rate of railway development in Britain dropped dramatically after World War I.

Above: *The London & North Eastern Railway were Cowans Sheldon's biggest customer for port-equipment, and orders like this one in 1931 were quite substantial. The order for seven 3-ton and one 5-ton coaling cranes for Grimsby fish docks were just a small part of the massive state-funded investment programme that benefited Cowans Sheldon during this period.*

Right: *Following the financial problems of the railways in the 1920s, investment in locomotive handling in the 1930s saw dozens of new turntables being supplied to the 'Big Four' railways in Britain. One example is this 60-ft dia. turntable, which is powered by the vacuum on the locomotive, in this case LNER A3 class 4-6-2 No. 2746* Fairwax.

Dove resigned as Managing Director in 1920 due to ill health, and was succeeded immediately by Mr. Pearson. The type of consolidation that followed was rather reminiscent of that when Dove senior had joined the firm 62 years earlier, the dividend increasing to between 15 and 20 percent in the following three years. The greatest order of the period was undoubtedly that for a 360-ton floating crane for Mitsubishi.

Another interesting order for the same period was two 80-ton boiler bogies for Hawthorn Leslie & Co. Meanwhile a 36-ton breakdown crane was constructed for the London & South Western Railway, and sent to the depot at Salisbury, where it remained until it was finally scrapped in the 1960s. During the next six years, the company received order after order, despite the fact that the full order book meant that delivery times were quite extended. Amongst these orders were a 150-ton Electric Floating Crane, for the Southern Railway at Southampton Docks, and a 40-ton electric travelling coaling crane ordered for the L&YR's Goole Dock.

A 20-ton wagon lifting cradle went to the London & North Eastern Railway, whilst the Australian State Railway ordered two 107-ton steam breakdown cranes in 1924. Meanwhile the Metropolitan Railway modernised its recovery fleet, with a 20-ton breakdown crane.

The LNER ordered a series of hydraulic locomotive wheel-drops, a consequence of J. B. Pearson's personal contacts coming to the fore. In the period 1923-5 no less than 67 new apprenticeship agreements were signed, helping the company to replace men lost in the past conflict - and ultimately preparing it for the next!

A consequence of World War I was the world-wide economic turmoil that followed, which affected almost every company in Britain as the 'slump' deepened. Cowans Sheldon were badly affected, and though orders still came in, some were taken well below cost. However, it was the coal strike that had the greatest effect for, without coal, the works were forced to shut down for a lengthy period in 1926.

Above: *With funding from the Government, in the 1930s the LMS placed a substantial order for coaling and ash plants. In the background, and beyond the 10-ton hand breakdown crane for the Mysore Railway in India, the steelwork for one of the LMS orders can be seen.*

Below: *Taken two weeks later. this view shows the top of one of the ash plants supplied to the LMS, with the winding drums and drive gear. The name of the contracting engineers, H. Lees appears painted in crude white letters on some of the steel work.*

The directors could not recommend a dividend that year, and things did not get much better before the end of the decade. Then, with the railway companies being awarded government money to combat the high unemployment, a major rail improvement began in the late 1920s. During a ten year period, over £315 million was spent in up-grading the railways, and a portion of this business came to Cowans Sheldon. Coaling plants and conveyors, larger turntables, wheel drops, wagon tipplers and the like were all supplied.

Undoubtedly the biggest single order was received from the LNER, who ordered no less than 37 electric quay cranes for Middlesborough docks, 10 level-luffing cranes for Grimsby docks, and a variety of marine cranes and capstans for their other ports. To cope with the expansion, the firm opened a London office in Bush House, under the management of one J. W. Branston.

Though Government-sponsored railway work artificially buoyed up the market, the depressed years of the 1930s meant a general downturn in the engineering industry. Cowans were not immune, and in 1933 the firm were forced to reduce all salaries by 10% until February 1935. However, the workers received other benefits, and in May the Recreation Ground was opened at Upperby. Railway work again proved the salvation, as the London Midland Scottish Railway placed five 70-ft diameter turntable orders for delivery in 1934. The LMS also contracted the firm to dismantle and re-furbish several ex-MR dock cranes at Heysham, then re-erect them at Fleetwood.

The Government in an effort to covertly support railway industries also directed some export business to Carlisle through the Chinese Purchasing Committee. They ordered two 30-ton steam breakdown cranes, locomotive-lifting jacks and a 30 metre turntable (the biggest constructed at the works). Four more 70-ft turntables were ordered for stock (5798-5801), but before the work was completed, no. 5799 was sold to the LMS for the shed at Aintree.

In 1935 Branston was appointed Assistant Managing Director, and a good working relationship developed with Pearson. Together the two men patented a Vacuum Engine for driving turntables, an invention that placed the company in a particularly advantageous position. By using its vacuum brake, a locomotive could turn a table with ease. Thus eliminating the need for hand-cranking or pushing that had been previously employed. True some turntables were still ordered for manual, electric or hydraulic operation, but the majority were now ordered with the vacuum drive.

Cowans Sheldon also supplied a conversion set for their earlier products, which enabled them to be changed to vacuum operation if the operators required. So popular were these types of conversion kits, that Cowans Sheldon constructed 100 for stock that year. During 1936 business picked up again, with orders being received from the LNER and LMS. The latter were improving locomotive depot facilities, and ordered five coaling plants to designs by Henry Lees & Co. for the motive power depots at Goole, Hellifield, Huddersfield, Mould, and Stafford.

The LNER also asked the firm to build a 50-ton electric Goliath crane for handling steel at Sheffield. They also purchased a steam breakdown crane that was out-shopped in just 11 weeks, and delivered to Tweedmouth in January. A 35-ton traverser was ordered by the GWR for Swindon works, along with ten 1-ton electric capstans for Birmingham. Though they were not very profitable, the years of 1935-6 saw a dividend of 5% paid to shareholders; this was followed by a 10% dividend up to 1939. The period leading up to World War II saw the retirement of J. W. Brown as Company Secretary, who was succeeded by Albert G. Topping the Chief Buyer.

Cowans Sheldon were now recognised as the world's leading supplier of railway and port lifting equipment, though as the shadow of war loomed, Ministry of Supply officials paid regular visits to the firm. All around the country production was being geared up at engineering workshops, and those in Carlisle were of particular interest as the Ministry felt that the city would be unlikely to come under aerial attack.

As St. Nicholas was the largest engineering works in the area, many orders were directed there. A major part of this work came from the Admiralty, and a section of the works were designated as a 'Lay Apart Store' and staffed by Naval ratings. A variety of naval equipment was constructed, including ship's lifeboats that were built in the joinery and fitting shops.

Two big orders were placed for railway and dock equipment for the Royal Navy at Singapore, but it fell before delivery and for some months the equipment lay around the works in an unfinished state. A 40-ton crane for the Malta dockyard was also cancelled because it was impossible to send it through the Mediterranean. On the other hand, numerous items of railway equipment were supplied as 'rush jobs' to replace installations that had been destroyed by bombing.

There were some unusual entries in the order book during this time, including one for the Ministry of Supply, which simply states 'Cost of storing 5-ton cranes at LMS Rly'. David Browns placed a number of orders with the firm, including several for gearbox casings for diesel-mechanical shunting engines. One interesting item was Vickers Armstrong's order for rifling gun barrel grooves. In 1943 the GWR placed their first major order for port equipment with Cowans, a 6-ton electric travelling crane for Barry Docks.

Early in 1944, a 70-ft articulated turntable was ordered by the LMS for Leicester, with a similar one going to the LNER at Dundee. More were ordered for the Woodhead Electrification scheme, but only the one for Darnall Shed was built at this time. Another order approved by the Ministry of Supply was a 60-ft diameter turntable for Brazil's Great Western Railway. This was an unusual order because the firm was strictly limited to manufacturing items for the home market.

Below: *The epitome of railway breakdown crane design between the two wars, is seen in this 45-ton crane built for the LNER, which was allocated to Doncaster in 1928. The crane is carried on what the LNER described as a two bogie, four axle carriage, whilst the jib runner is based on a 15-ton low-well truck.*

In 1945 the company returned to normal working, though for the first two years overseas orders were still strictly limited. Reconstruction work on railways and harbours accounted for a large proportion of the company's business. Each of the 'Big Four' placed orders, though the LMS and LNER placed the lion's share in the months leading up to the formation of British Railways.

In 1946 J. W. Branston retired after 42 years service, and was replaced by Major-General Sir John Kennedy KBE, CB, MC, who had been Director of Military Operations at the War Office and Assistant Chief to the Imperial General Staff. This also coincided with the announced retirement of J. B. Pearson, which was to take effect from December 1946. On his retirement the net liquid assets of the company stood at £242,000 (£7,260,000 at today's values), which is a stark contrast with the figure of £24,600 (£1,409,580) when he succeeded J.C. Dove in 1914. He was replaced as Managing Director by Major P. B. Tucker, who had been at the War Office in charge of Heavy Plant Maintenance. On arrival at Carlisle in 1947, Tucker re-arranged the works to meet the post-war situation. However, within a few months Sir John Kennedy found he had to tender his resignation when he was appointed as Governor of South Rhodesia.

Major Tucker did not last long either, and in 1948 he was succeeded by Philip Rambaut who joined Cowans Sheldon in 1935 after completing an engineering degree course at Cambridge University.

The last pre-nationalisation order was placed by the LMS in October 1947 for a 7$^{1}/_{2}$-ton overhead crane for Crewe Works, this was delivered to the Railway Executive the following March. The last order delivered to one of the 'Big Four', was a 6-inch parachute water tank for the LNER at Leeds. In March the following year, the first order from the Railway Executive was a 57-ft diameter turntable for Bournville. Two weeks later a 13' 6" dia. wagon turntable was ordered by the Southern Region,.but war damage-replacement work was limited in nature and not financially rewarding in substance.

A more unusual sale to BR is recorded in 1948, when the Recreation Ground was sold at a profit of £6,372 with the funds being given to the employees' welfare account. Pearson continued as Company Chairman, but the instability in management following the war caused him considerable concern. In 1950 he expressed these concerns as delivery dates continued to slide and trading profits dropped in a period when there were too many manufacturers chasing too few orders

Left: *This 1947 view shows work in progress, including the gearing for a 70-ft dia. turntable for New Zealand Government Railways (order 1906), and supports for orders 1900-1 (two 60-ft dia. balanced-on-centre turntables) for use in the colonies*

Top Right: *A lathe operator machining a spindle for an Australian Railways breakdown crane in 1954.* News Chronicle

Top Left: *A Cowans Sheldon patent wheel-drop system supplied to British Railways North Eastern Region in 1956, and seen here in 1959. The exact shed is not known, but ex-WD 2-8-0 locomotive No.90409 can be seen in the picture.*

The early 1950s were a difficult time, and the cost of living resulted in a 12.5% wage increase. As a consequence the firm's quotations compared unfavourably with most of their major competitors, and regretfully the company failed to win many of the orders that were being issued by the Railway Executive in its early days as part of the British Transport Commission. Business was no longer concluded on a personal level, as most of the new orders were awarded strictly to tender.

In 1950 only nine major BR orders were won, with eight each in the years 1951, 1952 and 1953, only three in 1954, and four in 1955. A number of minor contracts were awarded, but a tender for re-painting cranes showed the low-ebb which Cowans Sheldon had reached. When Pearson retired in 1953, Sir John Kennedy, replaced him following the completion of his term of office in Africa even though he had no engineering background and his contacts were limited to military and political circles. Even though he was unable to make a significant contribution to the business he remained in office until the re-organisation of 1961.

In 1954 the Company Secretary, A. G. Topping, retired and was replaced by N. S. Thompson until E.G. Hargreaves succeeded him in 1958. A dividend of 15% was paid throughout the 1950s, but the firm had ever increasing cash flow problems. On 1st November 1955, J. B. Pearson OBE passed away and his funeral was attended by a large number of employeess.

Delivery dates became more protracted, and the correspondence from this time reveals the development of a difficult relationship with BR. Overseas business continued, with a contract for an 80-ft diameter to the Egyptian Railways at Port Said. Tthis order caused its own problems and a large portion of the payments were never received, following President Nassar's nationalist stand that led to the outbreak of the Suez Crisis the following year. In 1956 a number of improvements were made in the works including refurbishment of the boiler shop, but already the writing was on the wall. In 1958 a firm of consultants undertook a survey of the works, though few of the workforce suspected it was the first move in the sale of the company.

Top Left: *Here we present a series of three pictures that show Cowans Sheldon's works and the company's attention to detail. Despite the sheer bulk and size of the items produced at St. Nicholas, there was nothing crude about the workmanship. Strict quality control and accurate measurement was essential to ensure that the high standards were maintained. Here we see a lathe operator using a large micrometer to check the diameter of a runner. The runner is part of the British Transport Commission breakdown crane order of 1959-60. This order called for a complete modernisation of the BR breakdown crane fleet after the internal enquiry that followed the Harrow & Wealdstone disaster of 1952 and found the breakdown crane arrangements to be inadequate (see also the picture on the bottom of page 35). ABMT*

Bottom Left: *One of the great advantages of Cowans Sheldon's longevity in the business, was the fact that all the drawings and foundry patterns were kept once a job was completed. The wealth of this information, although very rarely needed, proved essential when a customer ordered urgent 'non-standard' spares. Here a storeman finds out a wooden pattern in order to make a cast-steel pulley head for a customer in Ghana. The number and diversity of pattern types (each carefully numbered) can clearly be seen in the racks surrounding the storeman. Interestingly, even today customers will make contact with the works in Gateshead, or to Des-Cad in Carlisle to enquire about spare parts for items produced at the St. Nicholas works.*

Bottom Right: *Using optical alignment equipment, an engineer checks holes that have been reamed into main-frame girders.*

Right: *By the time that the company merged with the Clyde Crane, Booth Group, it had become established as a world leader in the field of railway and port equipment and its products were in universal service. Cowans Sheldon prided themselves as being able to replace any worn or broken component in the shortest possible time. Whether the customer was in Bradford or Bombay or (as shown here) Hartlepool, the objective was to get their equipment moving at the first possible opportunity. In this instance two engineers inspect the damage to the running gear of a dock crane supplied in 1948.*

Below: *One of the 75-ton steam breakdown cranes supplied by Cowans Sheldon & Co under the British Transport Commission's order of 1959. Works number C80 (BR RS1092/75) is seen here after allocation to Willesden depot (London), it shows the short-carriage crane, jib-relieving bogies and match truck DB998534. Had this substantial order been placed earlier, it may well have been the case that Cowans Sheldon would have remained an independent company.* British Railways London Midland Region

An amalgamation (in reality a take-over) was planned with the Clyde Crane & Booth Group, and minor reorganisation began at the end of 1958. From 1st January 1959 all the order numbers took on the pre-fix C; the first began at C1 (a 15-ft diameter wagon turntable for John Lysaghts at Scunthorpe which is pictured on page 51); whilst the last order under the old system was no. 10507 for a 10-ton electric travelling crane at Workington Docks.

Yet, in 1959 the firm began winning orders from the BTC for equipment under its modernisation programme, including the 30-ton and 75-ton breakdown cranes that had first been tendered for in 1955. In October orders were received for the 30-tonners (eight steam and two diesel), whilst in November ten steam and two diesel 75-ton cranes and 12 match-trucks were ordered. The London Midland Region also ordered two diesel-powered three-unit 12'-track layers.

Above: *The South Wales Steel Company's 85-ton diesel crane, was influenced by the 75-ton diesel hydraulic cranes designed for British Railways. It is seen here just after delivery, still awaiting its match-trucks, which were not ordered from Cowans.*

These self-propelled vehicles had three jib units, each of which was capable of being slewed 90° from the line of the track. A picture of one of these vehicles can be seen on page 54. January 1960 saw an order for a 68-ft electric traverser (160-ton s.w.l.) for the Byer Peacock works at Gorton. However, in May a letter was received from the BRB, stating:

'As a consequence of the current modernisation, and the likely withdrawal of all steam locomotives within the next ten years; all orders for turntables and water cranes, other than those specifically approved by the Executive Board are hereby cancelled.'

Top Right: *This 1954 order for a 50-ton civil engineer's bridging crane was placed by the Australian railways. Its specifications stated that it should also be capable of undertaking track clearing or breakdown work*

Bottom Right: *The demand for turntable equipment dropped as a result of British Railway's modernisation programme, which saw the widespread introduction of diesel locomotives and multiple units from the mid-1950s onwards. However, this interesting 1961 pose shows an ex-WD 2-8-0 locomotive, No.90514 on a Cowans 70-ft turntable at Thornton engine shed in Scotland.*

That was apparently the end of two product lines that the company had so successfully developed since the mid-19th century, but within two days an order was placed by London Regional Transport Executive for 4" water cranes. Orders were received for a number of wagon turntables following the merger, but these were mostly for industrial customers, overseas use or the Admiralty.

In October a 35-ton electric overhead crane was ordered for Derby Works, whilst two wagon turntables for Swindon were the last supplies to British Railways. An order was received for a crane from Sudan Railways, whilst an 85-ton diesel breakdown crane was ordered by the Steel Company of South Wales.

These proved to be the last railway orders tendered for by the independent firm, before absorption into Clyde Crane & Booth. The final three years were quite profitable, with 'after tax receipts' of around £132,000 in the three years to 1960. Early in 1961 the board accepted the offer of five Clyde Crane shares - after a free scrip issue of 'one for three' had been made to existing shareholders - plus two shillings in cash for each of the 150,000 £1 Cowans' shares.

At the time Clyde shares were valued at £1 3s 3d, thus making the value of each Cowans' share £4 10s 0d and the board duly recommended the deal to shareholders. The proposals would leave the manufacturing capacity unchanged, with Mr. Rambaut remaining as Managing Director at Carlisle. Kennedy would join the Clyde board as Deputy Chairman, and one other director would also be invited to join the board. An Extraordinary General Meeting approved the take-over, and compensation was authorised for the Directors' loss of office, but no staff were to be made redundant.

At the end of 115 years independent trading, it is interesting to note the extent to which the small business established by John Cowans and E. P. Sheldon had grown. The issued share capital was £150,000 in one pound shares, which in the late 1950s and early 1960s changed hands on the stock exchange at a rate between 46 shillings and 55 shillings per share. The top value in 1960 was 55s 6d, but even so, this was well below their true value, which according to the last balance sheet showed the shares to be worth 87s 9d. This was comprised up from a balance of £657,999 of which £365,000 was in current assets and the remainder in buildings, plant and machinery.

Above: *With the acquisition of Cowans Sheldon in to the Clarke-Chapman organisation, much-needed capitol was injected into the Carlisle operation, and new customers were found. The range of equipment was also modernised to meet the needs of the changes in industry, as the 1960s saw a gradual change from traditional heavy engineering. As industry re-equipped, and British Railways rid themselves of over 16,000 steam locomotives between 1956 and 1968, there came about a boom in the scrap metal industry. Under the Clyde Crane & Booth banner, two 7^1/$_2$-ton travelling cranes were supplied to Shepherds Scrap Metals. The vast array of debris beneath the cranes in this 1969 picture include the remains of old lattice signal posts, parts of steam locomotives, bits of an old drop forge hammer, old commercial vehicles and plant equipment, along with industrial boilers.*

Left: *The early 1960s saw a rapid big reduction in the purchasing power of British Railways, where a terminal decline had set in following the Beeching Report when hundreds of stations and many lines were closed. This directly affected the big railway crane makers, and to compensate for the loss of business they turned to the overseas markets. Not always stable by the 1960s, foreign business had to be treated warily, but in 1961 Cowans Sheldon were more than happy to receive an order for two diesel breakdown cranes for the Canadian mining firm Cartier. These were works orders C109 and C110, although they carried Cartier numbers and names. The larger crane was the 250-ton C3 Ursa Major, whilst C4 Ursa Minor was a 150-ton crane. In this view the larger of the two cranes has been brought out of the works for the first time - it is still the largest crane of its kind ever built.*

Left: *A view of one of the powerful 6-cylinder diesel engines fitted on the Cartier cranes.*

The new owners, had been formed in 1937 when the Motherwell firm of Clyde Crane & Engineering Co. had amalgamated with Joseph Booth of Leeds. By 1960 the firm had an issued capital of £225,000 in 4-shilling ordinary shares and a small number of redeemable preference shares. Their shares were changing hands at around £1 each prior to notice of the merger being announced. At that time the net book value of the Clyde group was £949,944, of which £525,886 was in current assets. The new Chairman of the group was Mr. J. B. Woodeson, who then presided over an organisation with assets of £1.6 million. It was the start of a new era for Carlisle's Crane-Makers, but also the beginning of the end. Whilst the account of what happened to Cowans Sheldon after 1961 is a complicated story, brief details of this period must be included for the sake of completeness.

Above: *An imposing view taken inside the St. Nicholas works, where we see three of the four bright yellow Ballast Regulators that were supplied to British Railways in the mid-1980s. These were the only four vehicles of this kind ever built by Cowans Sheldon and at the time of writing they are currently owned and operated by Centrac.*

In 1961, Cowans Sheldon had a total of 450 employees, and were one of the few crane manufacturers employing their own site staff. Clyde Crane and Booth merged with Cowans Sheldon, and the site services were increased. In 1969, Clarke Chapman acquired Cowans Sheldon, Clyde Crane & Booth, Wellman Cranes and Sir William Arrol. Following this, the railcrane business from the Rodley works in Leeds was transferred to Cowans Sheldon.

In 1982, Cowans Sheldon were merged with John Boyd, and were renamed Cowans-Boyd. But during the 1980s, Cowans were hit hard by the decline of the heavy industries, and the continued existence of the Carlisle operation had to be in question. Then in 1987, the St. Nicholas works were closed and manufacturing transferred to other factories in the group, although the design office team was to be retained in Carlisle.

Following the closure of the St. Nicholas Works in Carlisle, the manufacturing was carried out at the Clarke Chapman factory in Gateshead, Tyne & Wear. This ironically took the company back to the original 'Geordie' roots of its four founders. Design work was however carried on in Carlisle, as a pool of expertise existed in material handling equipment and it was both impractical and unnecessary to relocate all the design staff employees. The design team was relocated to a new suite of offices in the James Street Enterprise Centre, and it worked closely with the manufacturing operation on Tyneside.

Sadly the 1980s were not a good time for the British railway industry, and as the then Conservative government sought to privatise British Rail, a serious problem of under confidence developed within the industry. This book is not the place to discuss that situation, but not only did a lack of investment in the railways lead to the disastrous backlog of maintenance that exists to plague us down to today, but it saw fewer and fewer orders being placed for maintenance equipment. Clarke Chapman remained a player in the supply field, but by 1996 (and under the Rolls Royce Materials Handling banner) Cowans Sheldon had become purely a brand name as the design control was handed over to one of Clarke Chapman's sister companies. This was Callaird of Le Havre, France.

In 1996 Callaird/Cowans Sheldon won an order for four 140-ton rail cranes for Indian Railways. These were designed by Callaird, and built by Clarke Chapman Ltd. under the Cowans brand name. Then Clarke Chapman won an order from Railtrack to overhaul four of the existing 75-ton rail cranes under the Cowans banner. Despite this limited success, when Rolls Royce reorganised the business in 1998, they dropped the Cowans name from the product portfolio because it was not seen as being a core business product.

However, Martin Howells writes; 'By the back end of 1998 and early 1999, I was receiving useful enquiries which were not being processed so I approached the then Director of Manufacturing at Clarke Chapman, Kevin Johnson, who also felt we were missing a lost opportunity to put Cowans back where it should be!' This subsequent revival of the brand name coincided with Rolls Royce's requirement to sell the materials handling business, and their decision to close Callaird in 2000.

Above: *A celebration at St. Nicholas Works in the 1970s, as an official handover takes place between the company and British Railways. The order was for six 12-ton, three-axle civil engineer's cranes. These diesel-electric cranes would be used for track-laying, bridge repair and replacement or general lifting duties. The picture was taken after the testing and commissioning of the cranes, and two figures who were well-known in the company can be seen here; fourth from the left is Mr. Simon Baker, who was then the General Manager, whilst first from the right is Mr. George Langhorn who was the company's Chief Draughtsman. It will be noted that the crane does not prominently display the Cowans Sheldon name, but rather that of its parent company, the Clark Chapman - John Thompson Ltd., Crane & Bridge Division.*

A business plan was developed for the CS business and after being accepted, the company then actively approached various railways! Their first real break came in 2000, as Railtrack were looking for a Rail Delivery System. The new Cowans Sheldon team prepared their proposal, but were faced by design issues as they no longer had facilities to do this work in-house. They therefore returned to Carlisle, and began consultations with Descad.

This was, in fact, the former Cowans Sheldon Design team who had left the Rolls Royce Materials Handling business (circa 1998) to form Descad. Together they submitted their joint proposal in November 2000. In January 2001, the Clarke Chapman businesses including the Cowans Sheldon name was sold to the current owner Langley Holdings plc, and they formed Cowans Sheldon into a limited company and established a small project engineering team to operate it. By April 2001 the company were named as the preferred bidder and the following month they won their first order for £7.5m to supply eight Rail Delivery Systems and two Rail Carrier Sets. Cowans Sheldon were back in business once again!

Since then they have built up a relationship with Railtrack's successors, Network Rail, winning further contracts for overhaul and enhancements to four existing Long Welded Rail Trains. Then, following the presentation of proposals, they designed and manufactured six sets of Cable Drum Modules. These comprise a container-based module to deliver two 3-metre diameter 8-ton cable drums for use on the Southern Region electrification project. They have also been asked to design and manufacture nine Rail Head Treatment Train sets, comprising high-pressure jetting pump (14000psi) and water tanks, all built on container-based modules.

At the time of going to press, the company are also expecting an order to undertake a minimal overhaul of one of the old Cowans Sheldon 75-ton rail cranes, which has recently been taken out of 'mothballs' for use on the Southern Region electrification project. In all, that is some £22,000,000's worth of orders since being re-established in 2000. Obviously, a good name and a first class reputation still count for a lot, even in modern times.

Top Right: *The new 6-drum cable modules produced for Network Rail that are mentioned in the text.*

Bottom Right: *I had originally intended to place a picture of the St. Nicholas Works as they are today in this position, but if you have seen one MFI store or Burger King Drive-Thru, you probably wouldn't want to see those that are found on the site today! Anyway, here is a picture that proves that companies like Cowans Sheldon can still get orders based on the quality of their past products. In 1938 Cowans supplied a 75 ft turntable to the LNER at Marylebone, and 60 years later that turntable would get a new lease of life at the opposite end of the old LNER system. Thanks to the re-introduction of steam trains to the spectacular West Highland line, it was decided that a turntable was needed at the terminus (the tiny port of Mallaig) and the Highland Development Council contacted Clark Chapman Services to see if they could assist. As the picture shows, the answer was yes, and now authentic locomotive operation has returned to the Highlands.*

RAILWAY BREAKDOWN CRANES

As the railways developed, the need for transhipping freight by heavy lifting equipment became evident. Initially cranes were fixed in goods yards, warehouses or docks and used to transfer the freight in and out of railway wagons. Other cranes would be installed in railway workshops, and several engine sheds also had sheer-leg type cranes to lift locomotives during repair works.

Out on the tracks it was a different matter, and if a train came off the line it had to be re-railed as best the foot-platemen could. Levers, crude jacks and block and tackle (along with portable sheer-legs) sufficed until George England invented his traversing jack in 1839. Once this had been devised, many railways supplied two jacks on each locomotive - a practice that continued right into the early part of the 20th-Century.

Yet it was soon found to be more practical to have a special train for breakdown or re-railing work, and these began to be formed from the 1840s onwards. The first record of such a train (carrying tools, a travelling hand crane, and a riding van for the workmen) is on the Manchester & Leeds Railway. Although this seems to have been mostly used in the winter months in connection with re-railing trains derailed by ice and snow along the course of the arduous route through the heart of the Pennine mountains.

Quite when the breakdown train concept was firmly established is still undetermined, although the Great Western, the Sheffield, Ashton & Manchester and Caledonian railways all had permanent breakdown trains by 1847. All the cranes in these trains (many of which were made in Carlisle) were hand-operated, but capacities gradually increased. By 1855 at least 40 British railway companies had been supplied breakdown cranes by the Carlisle-based company.

The weight of locomotives and rolling stock was increasing all the time, and the performance of hand-operated cranes was limited to say the least. Yet from an early stage Cowans Sheldon were advocating the development of self-propelled steam-powered cranes. On page 10 we presented a view of one of the company's earliest steam cranes, and one of these was loaned to the Midland Railway for evaluation in 1857. Other steam travelling cranes were supplied to overseas customers, in Africa, South America and India, where they had a warm reception. More cranes were ordered by overseas railways, and several were purchased for use in Britain by both railway contractors and reservoir builders. No appreciable orders were placed by the railways, although the Midland again had two for evaluation in 1874 after seeing similar cranes being used in the construction of their Settle & Carlisle Railway.

In 1876 two 5-ton steam travelling cranes were bought for breakdown work on this mountainous line, and these are the first such cranes known to be purchased by a main line British railway. Other railways soon followed, and by 1896 Cowans had supplied no less than 154 'breakdown' cranes for use in Britain - an average of one crane rolling out of the St. Nicholas works every seven weeks.

Capacities increased to 30-tons by World War I, and 45/50-tons by World War II, and finally 70-tons when the last big steam crane orders were placed by BR in the 1960s. Overseas the capacities were greater, and cranes of over 100-tons were common. In Britain diesel cranes of 105-tons were supplied to BR, and at the same time the last steam cranes were either scrapped or converted to hydrostatic transmission and diesel engines.

However, the increase in overhead electric catenary limited the use of railway breakdown cranes, and reliance started being placed on road cranes with telescopic jibs. Yet, in the late 1970s, Cowans Sheldon and BR led the world with the first 75-tonne high capacity diesel hydraulic boom rail cranes employing technology used on road vehicles. The boom on these cranes was a fully-welded box of high tensile material with plate thickness uo to $1^5/8$ inch. Along with a series of 12-tonne General Purpose cranes, this technology would take the British application of the product range up to the end of the 20th Century.

Top Left: *Works order 8500 was a 36-ton breakdown crane for South African Railways in 1899. Note the travelling position of the chimney, which was hinged in order to allow clearance beneath bridges and other over-line structures.*

Top Right: *During World War I orders were confined to the 'home' market and overseas business was limited. This 2' 6" gauge 7-ton hand breakdown crane was built as a special order for the Gaekwars Baroda State Railway (India). In the background can be seen several Leyland lorries being bodied for the Royal Navy.*

Bottom Right: *In 1924 the Metropolitan Railway decided to improve its breakdown train service, and ordered a 25-ton steam crane from the Carlisle-based firm.* Author's Collection

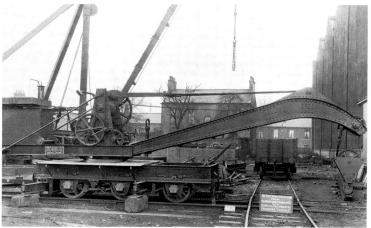

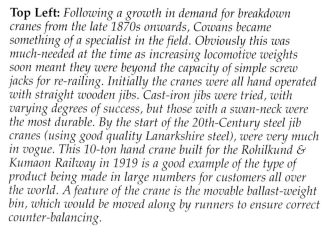

Top Left: *Following a growth in demand for breakdown cranes from the late 1870s onwards, Cowans became something of a specialist in the field. Obviously this was much-needed at the time as increasing locomotive weights soon meant they were beyond the capacity of simple screw jacks for re-railing. Initially the cranes were all hand operated with straight wooden jibs. Cast-iron jibs were tried, with varying degrees of success, but those with a swan-neck were the most durable. By the start of the 20th-Century steel jib cranes (using good quality Lanarkshire steel), were very much in vogue. This 10-ton hand crane built for the Rohilkund & Kumaon Railway in 1919 is a good example of the type of product being made in large numbers for customers all over the world. A feature of the crane is the movable ballast-weight bin, which would be moved along by runners to ensure correct counter-balancing.*

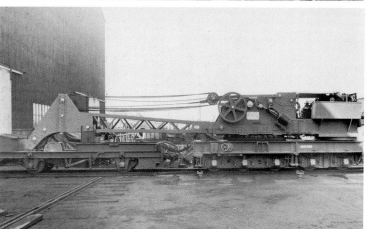

Centre Left: *This metre gauge 35-ton steam breakdown crane was built by Cowans Sheldon inside seven months, and outshopped in February 1946. Throughout the build programme a level of considerable urgency was applied to the job, for it was required for the Burma railway system. Systematically destroyed and ripped up to be used elsewhere, Burma's railways were in an atrocious state at the end of World War II. Thousands of prisoners of war, along with conscripted native Burmese had been used to build the Japanese military lines through dense jungles and steaming swamps, with a massive cost in human life and suffering. To achieve rebuilding, large quantities of mechanised equipment were obtained.*

Bottom Left: *On a dull November day in 1932, we see No. 5232 a 36-ton steam breakdown crane. It was originally ordered by the LMS for allocation to their Stafford MPD, but before it was completed the company transferred it to their Northern Counties section in Ireland. This decision was taken in light of a spate of accidents on the LMS in the early 1930s, which revealed that cranes of 30-ton to 40-ton capacity were inadequate for the tasks they were facing. Also with the advent of larger, more powerful engines being built following William Stanier's appointment as Chief Mechanical Engineer in January 1932, the LMS decided to up-rate its standard breakdown crane to 50-tons. Trials of the crane were undertaken at Kingmoor Depot in Carlisle and along the former Glasgow & South Western Railway in the Annan and Dumfries areas. It was eventually shipped to Northern Ireland via Stranraer.* Courtesy C. Dobson

Top Right: *In addition to Burma, a large number of railway systems had been devastated during the war years. Even where lines had escaped enemy action, infrastructure, motive power and rolling stock had been heavily used and prematurely worn out. Accidents increased and new works were long overdue. Cowans Sheldon were well aware of the potential orders that could come from this situation, and they took advantage of the Labour governments exhortation to 'export or die'. This 5' 6" gauge 20-ton breakdown crane for the Indian Government (G.I.P.) Railway is a product of that era and it dates from April 1950. It had been ordered prior to the granting of Indian independence with a delivery date of 1949, but delays arose due to numerous changes in the trading relationships between Britain and India after 1947.*

Centre Right: *The Indian sub-continent had always been a good area for the Carlisle-built cranes. Initially influenced by British engineers working in Asia, the business was of extremely great value. At one stage in 1895 no less than 24 cranes were on the order books for the Indian railways. By the 1960s, the Indian independence and the formation of the twin states of Pakistan (east and west) had changed the climate considerably. Nevertheless, when four new 65-ton breakdown cranes were required for the Western Pakistan Railway, the order was placed in distant Carlisle. Here we see the first of the four cranes, works No.C392, to be turned out at St. Nicholas. The match-truck is given a low-load height, and is also fitted with a large capacity water tank in view of the vast distances between water columns in some areas. The reserve water tank had a feed pipe leading to the crane boiler.*

Bottom Right: *Slightly earlier than the Pakistan crane order, Cowans received its order for the South Wales Steel Company. Pictured here in 1966 is the 70-ton diesel crane built to works number C207, it is seen near the steel works with a jib truck made from a converted BR wagon. Despite the fact that Cowans quoted an inclusive price for match trucks and jib runners, the Steel Company knew it could obtain supplies much cheaper in its own locality. At places like Bridgend, Barry, Newport and Risca, hundreds of redundant British Railway wagons were awaiting scrapping. Some of these were only a few years old, and could be bought relatively cheaply. Here we see that a crippled wagon truck was eventually acquired for the task of jib carrier and it clearly looks out of place. Furthermore, whilst the crane still looks to be in a good order, the picture reveals that rust is rapidly showing through on the jib-truck.*

Top Right: *During World War II the LMS was in need of several light-load travelling cranes for the CCE's department as it found its resources stretched by the emergency repair work occasioned by enemy air-raid action. To this end the LMS ordered fifteen 6-ton well-type hand cranes. Several more were later ordered by the Ministry of Supply and were sent out to France after June 1944.* Author's Collection

Bottom Left: *The capability of being able to undertake civil engineering work was a secondary requirement for all railway breakdown cranes, and it was a common occurrence for the CCE to requisition the use of a crane for routine maintenance work - particularly bridging. An interesting example of this work is this view dating from December 1959, showing a pair of Cowans Sheldon cranes (one ex-LMS and one ex-LNER) working on a new over-line road bridge for the A1M (Doncaster- By-pass).* Dowsett Associated Group of Companies

Bottom Right: *British Railways' reluctance to adopt diesel-powered cranes is hard to understand, given the haste to introduce diesel locomotives during the 1960s. However, out of the batch of cranes purchased by the British Transport Commission, 30-ton and 75-ton diesel cranes were ordered for evaluation. One of each DB965186 (C89 75-ton) and DB96183(C66 30-ton) are seen here at Raynes Park in 1967 on civil engineering work.* Peter Tatlow

Below: *The awesome lifting ability of a locomotive breakdown crane is clearly demonstrated by this 107-ton Cowans Sheldon breakdown crane built for the South African Railways.*

Above: *On these two pages we present a series of pictures showing Cowans Sheldon railway cranes in action. First of all we see a 45-ton crane for the Indian State Railways being tested at the St. Nicholas Works. Information printed on the back of the photographs states; 'The simulated load of 28³/4-tons and the packing has been set up in such a way as to test the cant on the crane - essential to ensure that the crane will remain on its tracks during the heavy lifting work it will have to undertake once it is sent to India where it will help reconstruct those railways that were heavily worked during the war'*

TURNTABLES

In the early days of railways, facilities had to be provided at the termini stations for turning round locomotives in order that they could set off on their next journey facing the 'right way'. These devices, called turntables, were situated at the end of the platform, but they often connected to a cross line that was constructed at right angles to the arrival line. This would then connect to another table on an adjacent line, so to 'turn' one of the small engines of the day, the crew would rotate the table 90° to allow access on to the 'cross or traversing' line.

The locomotive would then be run across to another table and be turned a further 90° on to the 'releasing line'. These cross lines might include a number of tables, for example the station at Derby had no less than eight, with the cross line connecting to the engine shed. Although this arrangement did not last long in passenger termini, it served a useful function in many goods yards and warehouses down to the 1960s. As locomotives increased in size these early wooden plate tables were no longer practical, so the use of cast-iron girders was introduced for the new 20 to 30 feet tables that replaced them.

In these early turntables stout cross-braced girders would form the basis for the deck, and they would be connected to a heavy central pivot that was set deep into the ground. In more modern times these girders were usually set below the table deck, and this necessitated a deep well into which the table would be set. However, far more popular (at least up to the 1880s), was the 'bridge' turntable, where the girders were set above the deck. Usually the girders would be arched (sometimes known as bow-string) in order to support the weight they were expected to carry.

By the end of the 19th century the size and weight of locomotives had increased to such an extent that the problems of weight and balancing became ever more important. These problems were further aggravated when tables were extended in length, with diameters increasing to around 50 to 55 feet.

Some new railways (the GCR being the classic example in Britain) built tables to the larger size, but many others compromised and just bought an extension kit to achieve the extra length. Unfortunately these 'lengthened tables' were prone to jamming and they did not have a long life.

Initially all the tables had been 'turned' by hand so a fair degree of skill was required to get the loco in the right spot. Then came geared windlasses with winding handles, which still required a lot of human effort and skill. These types were still less than adequate for the big express types introduced after World War I, so they were replaced by geared drive tables with some form of traction motor or engine. Basically the two main types of traction were either electricity or power taken from a locomotive's vacuum. We can perhaps illustrate the development of turntable technology with four photographs of turntables supplied to the 'Big Four' during the 1930s.

Opposite. *This is a picture that I have used in two of my other books, yet it is not only a superb and evocative image, but it also illustrates the best in Cowans Sheldon turntables as well. Installed at King's Cross Top Locomotive Shed to accommodate Nigel Gresley's A3 class Pacifics in 1927, the equipment had to be 'uprated' to turn the new A4 class locomotives on their introduction in 1935. This photograph, probably taken in early 1936, shows one of the new A4 class 4-6-2s, No. 2512* Silver Fox, *on the turntable with the newly installed vacuum tractor. Comparing this LNER turntable with the GWR's at Paddington shows the much neater position of the air-cylinder, which was possible because of the deeper well at King's Cross.*

Top Right: *As the 20th century dawned, turntables were mostly confined to locomotive depots, but the sizes and capacities increased. The GWR turntable outside London's Paddington station with a vacuum tractor and large cylinder seen just after installation with Hall Class 4-6-0 No.7910* Hown Hall.

Centre Right: *A 45-ft LMS turntable, seemingly devoid of locomotives but actually surrounded by Fowler and Stanier types including Jubilee class 4-6-0* Manitoba. *It is seen in this September 1938 view, and it will be noted that the turntable well has been painted white as part of the preparations for the forthcoming 'Black Out' regulations which would be introduced a year later.*

Bottom Right: *The practice of having turntables at the end of each branch line reduced dramatically from the 1870s onwards, especially with the development of ubiquitous tank engines that could operate in either direction without the need for turning. Even so, some small termini stations retained the facility as for example this one at Chatham. No money was spent on uprating this turntable, presumably due to the Southern Railway's extensive electrification programme which involved multiple unit trains, which did not need turntables. Even so the task of pushing locomotives round by hand, such as this L1 Class 4-4-0 No.31753, was by no means an easy one!*

The subject of turntables is absolutely massive, and one suspects that it should form a book in its own right. Indeed as far as the modelling enthusiast is concerned, there is a great need for such a book, because most of the proprietary models that have been commercially produced are far removed from the prototypical British railway turntable. Outwardly there was very little overall standardisation in turntable design, yet firms like Cowans Sheldon did go some way to achieving this amongst their clients, and towards the end of the 19th century the tables being supplied to British railways like the Midland, North British and Great Central (as well as many foreign systems) all had the same basic design. Indeed a study of the company's drawings from 1857 onwards will reveal that the standardisation of parts was far wider than a cursory glance of photographs of the finished products would suggest.

Cosmetically the majority of turntables looked different, but in reality they had quite a lot in common. A study of the order book and sales records will also show that, by the 1860s, Cowans Sheldon were actively leading (almost dictating) their customers along certain roads towards a 'recommended' product. Yet it was not until nationalisation of Britain's railways in 1948 that real standardisation was achieved.

There had been some moves towards this goal by the 'Big Four' in the 1930s, and certainly orders placed by the Railway Executive during World War II had shown what could be achieved. Yet already the market was in decline in many overseas countries, as steam gave way to diesel and electric traction. In countries like India, Africa and other parts of the British Empire, steam was still in full swing so the market had not completely disappeared. Sizes continued to get bigger, and 70- to 80-ft diameter turntables were being supplied.

Accordingly, the problem of balance became even more important, so the newer turntables were built with articulated steel girders and a three-point suspension system. But Cowans had already developed 'free-movement' and their turntable wells would be accurately levelled and the outer-race rails positioned to very fine tolerances. Ball bearings (or in some cases taper roller bearings) would be fitted to the outer-race wheels, and a ball race fitted to the central pivot so that turning was an easy task. The well known incident when the Garsdale turntable was so well-balanced that it blew round and round in a gale (retold in Rev Wilbur Awdry's 'Thomas The Tank Engine' story *Troublesome Engines*), illustrates just how free running turntables had become.

Top Left: *A really marvellous example of a standard British Transport Commission electric turntable, seen here at Thornaby Depot on Teesside in the late-1950s. Yet in other ways this view is really a pointless picture, for the new forms of traction like this Type 2 BR diesel (D5153) simply did not require the services of a turntable (although we should state that turntables still have some use for turning multiple unit driving cars and HST power units).*

Top Right: *The earliest on-centre balance turntables of the 1860s were little more than circular wooden plates, with rails laid across. Although more sophisticated systems came later on, it should be recalled that primitive turntables were still being made for other applications besides locomotive turning right into the mid-20th century. Wooden wagons turntables were the main example, but steel-sector plates were also made for industrial use, including vehicle turntables for use in garages. Order No. C1 was a 14-ft wagon turntable to drawing DX14 for the chemical company of John Lysaghts at Scunthorpe. It is pictured in November 1961, with a somewhat battered 8-ton wagon being turned by hand. If you can mentally replace the image of the wagon with an early steam engine, this would have been the scene you would have witnessed on most early railways.*

Centre Right: *Whilst all the examples of turntables shown thus far have featured well-type models, this example shows a bridge turntable. Built for the Central Argentine Railway in 1914 to order 2036, this unit had a diameter of 70-ft. The photograph is a particularly good illustration of the engineering practice employed. First of all it will be seen that the bridge is basically a series of girder plates riveted together, and it is interesting to note that several of the same jig-built plates were used (in an inverted position) on well-type turntables. The plate steel deck is another forward thinking example of technology, as most British railways were still specifying wooden decks. Finally the outer girder ends and the running wheels can be seen. The flange-mounted roller bearings on this model were located at either end of the short axle carrying the race wheels.*

Bottom Right: *The end of turntable manufacture was signalled by BR's decision to change from steam traction to diesel and electric locomotives, both of which usually had driving positions at either end. Accordingly, we return to Thornaby for this picture of the depot's round-house in December 1961 to illustrate the demise of the turntable. As the steam scrapping programme begins to build in momentum, the occupants of stalls 11, 12, and 14 have been put into store. Though all the engines were later returned to service, the growing allocation of Type 2 and Type 4 diesel classes meant that the reprieve was short-lived. Whilst the Class V2, No 60911 is repeating a familiar railway task as it backs out on the turntable, it is the end of an era, not only for the locomotives but also the equipment and the firms like Cowans Sheldon that supplied it.*

TRAVERSERS

From the description of early turntables and traversing lines given on page 48, it will be appreciated that it was only a very small step to the development of a piece of traversing equipment. Basically traversers (or transfer tables as they are called in some countries) were travelling rail bridges, or simply rails braced together, on to which a locomotive or piece of stock could be placed. Located at right angles to the track, a set of lines in a pit would carry these bridges by sliding them to the next available line.

Of course these bridges could not turn a locomotive or piece of stock, but they were quite widely employed at a variety of locations in the early days, including passenger and goods stations. Indeed several traffic traversers remained down into British Railways ownership, and the last known survivor was at Birmingham's Moor Street freight depot, which lasted until 1966 or 1967. However, throughout the 20th century, the main application for traversers was in the railway workshops. At these locations the traversers did sterling work, and a few are still in position down to this day.

Recently much wider use has been made of overhead travelling cranes, and traversers are now far fewer in number. Most of the remaining traversers are 90 to 100 feet in length, and these can accommodate the most modern rail vehicles, but for many years the overall length was usually 50 to 60 feet. In this regard the railway manufacturing plants faced a rather severe problem, as the overall length of their finished products was dictated by the size of their traversers.

An example of this will be found in the London & North Western Railway's policy of producing railway carriages with a maximum length of just 42 feet, when its competitors had already begun making much longer carriages. Yet few will appreciate that this constraint was dictated to them by the length of their 45 feet traversers in the workshops. For the same reason, this is one of the primary factors as to why British freight vehicle wheelbases stayed at a maximum of 15 feet for so long. Quite simply, when the world's railways were building much larger freight vehicles, Britain's workshops were limited by their fixed equipment.

Top Left: *This picture admirably shows how a traverser system works, and once seen it is very easy to grasp the principle. This is pictured at the Gorton (Manchester) works of Byer-Peacock, with the 90-ft locomotive traverser supplied by Cowans in 1960. On the traverser one of the recently completed 'Hymek' hydraulic diesel locomotive for BR's Western Region. This particular example is D7001, but two other members of the class can just be seen inside the shops behind it, with D7003 on the left and D7000 on the right. The traverser, of course, forms the common bridge between the workshop roads and the outlet lines.*

Top Right: *British Railway's wagon workshops at Walker Gate on Tyneside, with Cowans Sheldon traverser C112, supplied in 1960 to yet another BTC modernisation order. Even so, this was only a 15-ft traverser, and the concept of larger freight vehicles had not been thought through as far as repair facilities were concerned. Strangely, and the reason for this can not be understood, British companies did not progress the development of longer traversers until well into the second part of the 20th century. By contrast, Cowans Sheldon were building 25 feet wagon and 100 feet coach traversers for foreign applications in the late19th-Century. One example of a locomotive traverser for China in the 1920s was for one of 95 feet in length with a maximum capacity of 175-tons. Therefore this example is still quite primitive in comparison with what other countries were using. Note the hauling winches, control cabin and (on the extreme left) the lattice tower for the over-head current collection.*

Centre Right: *An electric traverser of the type supplied to several railway companies around the world - this one just happens to be located outside C shop in the Great Western Railway workshops at Swindon. This picture well illustrates the value of the traverser concept, as it easily allows the movement of rail vehicles at angles to the workshop roads despite the cramped nature of this extensively developed site. It is also an interesting order, in that Cowans Sheldon never had much success selling equipment of any kind to the Great Western Railway, nor to its successor the Western Region of British Railways.*

Bottom Left: *This Cowans Sheldon traverser is seen at the Abbey Works of Clayton's Railway, Carriage & Wagon Co. in the early 1920s. The recently out-shopped Pullman Car Cambria is pictured on the traverser shortly after it was installed in 1920/1. The works order for this 70-ft. traverser was No. 159. This makes this piece of equipment unique, as it was the last traverser to be built to the old order numbering system which had been introduced by J.C. Dove upon his being made works manager at St. Nicholas. It is also interesting that Clayton opted for this 70-ft model, at a time when most British railway workshops were limiting themselves to 60-ft. traversers.*

TRACK EQUIPMENT

The production of other forms of ancillary equipment was something that Cowans Sheldon prided themselves on. If a railway wanted a piece of kit, the enterprising Carlisle company would try and build it. One of the most notable orders in the book was for 'spare fire bars and new cast-firebox grate' for the Earl of Carlisle's Railway at Hallbankgate. The locomotive on to which it was fitted was none other than Stephenson's world famous Rocket, which came to Cumberland after its short working life with the Liverpool & Manchester Railway.

It was for the same railway that Cowans made their first piece of track equipment, in the form of a ballast discharge wagon in 1872. This wagon was fitted with a fabricated steel body, with sloping inner walls leading to a bottom discharge door. Two adjustable rollers were fitted on the wagon axles, and it is presumed that these formed some sort of 'tamping' function to pack the ballast. Few other details remain about this fascinating vehicle, and no drawings or photographs exist, and the only substantial information about it was found in the St. Nicholas spares order book. Yet it was some while before Cowans actually began producing track equipment from the main line railways.

It is indicative of the company's efforts that, in the years ever since, they have endeavoured to produce whatever equipment their customers required. Not only would they do this, but they would also often do so entirely from scratch, by analysing the customer's needs and special requirements, then drawing up designs for their approval. Very often these would be British railways, at least in the early years, but not exclusively so. The research and development was often ground-breaking, and the designers and engineers at Cowans Sheldon gained a reputation second to none.

It was not surprising that, as track laying and permanent way maintenance changed from the old fashioned gangs of manual labourers, the company would be asked to provide new mechanical equipment for the job. The use of pre-fabricated track sections with concrete sleepers had been pioneered in Britain during World War II, with 'panels' being made up away from the site where they were need and then transferred there by rail. Handling these panels by rail crane was of course quite feasible, but the London Midland Region of British Railways asked Cowans to produce a machine for the job and thus was born the three-unit tracklayer, what followed was of course a natural order of progression.

Left: *In the BTC modernisation programme, several items of track-laying equipment were ordered for evaluation, but the first items that Cowans produced were not approved for use on British Railways. However as two of these three-unit tracklayers were supplied 'on trial and evaluation' to the London Midland Region, valuable experience was gained by both the maintenance crews and the manufacturer.*

Top Right: *Though the BTC tracklayers were not a great success, they did form the basis from which future track-laying equipment would be developed. The basic concept was their ability to lift entire sections of track from where it lay and place it on to flat wagons, and then replace the removed section with a new 60-foot long panel of pre-fabricated track. The concept for the three-unit tracklayer was therefore considerably ahead of its time, but after evaluation the design was not approved. Yet it did provide a basis for what followed as the picture below clearly illustrates.*

Centre Right: *Son of the father! In this view of a Cowans Sheldon Twin Jib Tracklayer, you can clearly determine the progression from the three-unit machines. These on-track machines were ideal for track panel replacement on sections of line where multiple tracks were located. The self-propelled machines had the benefit of telescopic jibs and offered a large number of application possibilities to the operator. Where lines were just single tracks, another piece of equipment, the Single Line Gantry (not illustrated) was designed to relay track at a rate of 200 metres per hour, the same as the twin jib units.*

Bottom Right: *Of course, sectional track panels were just one element of the way that railways would develop and, in view of the higher levels of maintenance required by shorter sections of track, the long welded rail technique was introduced. To meet the special demands of laying lengths of rail around 180 metres long, a train had to be designed for the job. The result was a self-propelled vehicle that could simultaneously position two lengths of 183 metre rails on to the rail track at the same time. The Cowans LWRT 180 equipment consists of a stabling wagon, with lookout or guard's cab, nine adapted flat wagons, a powered wagon and a chute wagon with operator's cab. A rail handling gantry unit with a full length cab completes the equipment, and this provides protection for the operatives when boarding or alighting the train. The gantry runs on rails positioned on the side frames of the rail-carrying wagons and can traverse the full length of the train thanks to bridging units between the wagons. Eight of the wagons are fitted with two roller frames, each of which has a four-tier Guide Roller. With a capacity of six rails per tier, the train has a capacity of a total of 24 rails per train. The ninth wagon is fitted with a clamping system to secure the rails when the train is in motion.*

Overhead Cranes

The development of the overhead crane is very easy to trace, and from the evidence there can be little doubt that E.P. Sheldon had a great deal to do with the concept. During a conversation with Robert Stephenson at his works in Newcastle, Sheldon was asked if he could devise a means of improving the sheer-leg arrangement for lifting locomotive boilers on to the engine frames. Block and tackle had been employed, but this had tended to jam or tangle during the lift.

It is said that Sheldon came up with the idea of mounting the block and tackle below a small four-wheeled truck, and then running the truck on a set of rails just below the workshop roof. Quite what date this event occurred is lost in the mists of time, but as Sheldon was still a young man at the time, it may have occurred before he even left Stephenson's employ. Once the engineer had established his factory at Woodbank, the overhead crane became one of the early product lines and the first was supplied to Ireland in 1859, but the first big capacity orders came in 1863 for the Inverness & Aberdeen and NER railways.

It is assumed that the early orders were 'square shaft rope-operated' gantry cranes that would span one or more railway tracks, and extend over roads or canals in order to effect a straight lift out of one type of transport into another. Some of these cranes had ladle buckets (for carrying coal etc.), some had hooks, whilst yet others had simple slings or block and tackle. Yet they all had one thing in common, the ability to lift an item of freight, and slide it effortlessly across to another form of transport in order to effect trans-shipment.

Later on, steam, then electric cranes were developed and these are illustrated in the accompanying photographs. Initially the cranes were fixed in a single location, but later they were able to run along short sections of track. The overhead crane is still in widespread use around the world today, notably in engineering factories, nuclear power plants, or anywhere that heavy items require moving a relatively short distance. They are widely used with containerised traffic, and can be seen in ports, rail terminals, and road haulage depots all over the world.

Top Left: *A 25-ton Goliath crane supplied to the LMS in 1925, sold to Derby, and is believed to have been erected in Staffordshire (possibly Walsall?) - further details would be appreciated. The versatility of the traversing overhead crane is seen here, as a pressure container is off-loaded from a railway 'well-wagon'. It will then be loaded on to the LMS lorry, which is an AEC Y-Type with a Derby-built wooden cab.* LMS Official

Top Right: *The Goliath crane pictured here was erected not far from Carlisle, and was the very terminus of the line that ran out to the Solway coast. Beyond Silloth station an extension of the line branched off to serve the Vickers-Armstrong gun-testing range at Bliterlees. The travelling crane would lift gun barrels off the incoming railway wagon, and then traverse a short section of track to place the piece of ordnance on to a gun mounting. The gun would be tested by firing shells out into the sea.*

Bottom Right: *One of the company's overhead electric cranes that had originally been built for steam power. Examples of this type of crane were supplied to several railway workshops, including Swindon, Crewe, and the North British Loco, as well as several foreign railways. This one is thought to have been purchased by the North Eastern Railway, and if so it would either be the one located at Hull Docks or on Teesside (location not confirmed). Under the gantry one of the NER's Sentinel steam lorries can be seen in the process of loading steel.*

Bottom Left: *Brunswick Dock Goods Depot, Liverpool with a 40-ton Travelling Goliath crane supplied by Cowans Sheldon to the British Transport Commission as part of the railway modernisation programme. Note the imposing Cheshire Lines warehouse in the background.* British Railways, London Midland Region

Dock Cranes

The dock crane is probably one of the earliest pieces of mechanisation applied in the transport industry. They were known to the Phoenecians, Egyptians, Babylonians and Romans to name but a few of the early civilisations. Most were of the sheer-leg or tripod design, with a central pulley at the apex of the crane legs. A hook would be swung out to the waiting vessel, where it would be caught by a seaman and lowered in to the vessel's hold. Once attached to an item of freight or a cargo net, the shore crew would haul away on the ropes until the cargo cleared the hold. The ships crew would, by the use of ropes, control the cargo as it was allowed to swing back to a vertical position under the crane. The cargo would then be lowered to the quayside for onward movement. The concept remained in use for many years, and the huge example shown left is probably the ultimate development of the sheer-leg or tripod method.

Progress in dock cranes owes much to the development of the railways, and with it the need to load and unload merchant vessels more rapidly than had been the case in the days of horse and cart. Cranes that handle much heavier loads, demanded a whole new concept in crane design. Furthermore, cranes that could traverse the length of the wharves were an obvious advantage, whilst movable or rotating jibs were also essential. The subject is far too complex to cover in this small publication, but we hope that the following pictures will give some idea of the involvement of Cowans Sheldon in this fascinating industry.

Left: *With the opening of the Stockton & Darlington Railway in September 1825, the mine-owners and waggonway operators of the North East began to look at building competing railways to get coal down to the rivers Tees, Tyne, and Wear. To illustrate progress in cranage at the inter-change points between rail and sea, we might consider three examples of Cowans Sheldon-built dock cranes. First we see an 80-ton sheer leg steam crane ordered in 1880, and believed to have been erected on the River Tees where its height is around 70-ft above the quayside.*

Top Right: *With the opening of the Stanhope & Tyne Railroad in 1834, between Stanhope, Consett and the Tyne, a new route brought coal, pig iron and limestone down to the river east of Gateshead. A new port opened up at the terminus of the railway, and it became known as Tyne Dock. The picture shown here illustrates eight 3-ton electric level-luffing cranes. Four of these were installed in 1936 (Nos. 5384-7), and four more were installed in 1940 (Nos. 7286-9). Note the Ministry Of Transport iron-ore tippers being loaded in readiness for a working to the Consett steel works.*

Bottom Right: *Typical of the post-war orders for dock equipment supplied by Cowans are these 6-ton level-luffing electric travelling cranes, flour of which were erected at Sunderland for the River Wear Commissioners in 1957.*

Top Left: *As Cowans Sheldon moved into the port-equipment field, it found several customers amongst the railways it supplied. Many of these owned or had interests in ports, docks and harbours. One example, the Great Central Railway, built a massive dock complex on the River Humber at Immingham. The dock equipment was purchased exclusively from Cowans Sheldon, and the LNER continued the tradition when it purchased these cranes in 1946.* General Electric.

Bottom Left: *Hoisting aloft a Scammell semi-trailer, a 6-ton wharf crane at Preston docks loads the MV* Bridge Ferry (the first purpose-built Irish Sea ro-ro ferry), *whilst two more box van semi-trailers (Pickfords and Lotus-Delta Shoes) wait their turn.* Port Of Preston Authority

Bottom Right: *This 6-ton wharf crane was purchased by the South African Railways for Cape Town where it unloads the twin screw motor vessel* Union Castle *in 1958.*

Top Right: *In 1957 a spate of new orders were won, including several new wharf cranes and low-luffing cranes for the Mersey Docks & Harbour Board. Here we see a 6-ton crane just after erection. By the way, the storage tanks in the background do not hold oil, only molasses.* Mersey Docks & Harbour Board

Bottom Left: *The size of dock crane bodies cannot always be appreciated when viewed from the ground, but inside the erecting shop at Carlisle the scale can be gauged far better. This 1948 picture shows one of the larger crane bodies, but we can not identify the customer, and nothing in the order book gives any clue as no work of this type was being carried out at that time. The turntable in the foreground, an 80-ft. dia. table for Nigerian Railways, confirms the actual date as being March 1948.*

Bottom Right: *In the period 1880--1930 many travelling dock cranes were in the 10- to 15-ton capacity. As for example the one on Battery Quay, Douglas, Isle of Man that Cowans Sheldon supplied in 1884. For years this limited the maxmum load that could be lifted from vessels to 15-tons. Therefore all the island's machinery, railway engines and so on could not be sent in parts weighing more than 15-tons. To rectify this the Isle of Man Harbour Commissioners ordered this 25-ton steam travelling crane with a vertical boiler in 1949. It was eventually taken out of service in the early 1980s, when safety concerns were aired about its operation due to the close proximity of a petrol storage facility, even though it was changed to an oil-fired boiler before its demise. However, its cab and boiler were well appreciated by the dockers, who used to dry off inside the cab on wet days. Ironically its driver of many years was called Frank Cowan!*

The advances that Cowans Sheldon were making for commercial dock and ship-building companies soon began to interest other maritime concerns. One important customer to begin placing orders with the Carlisle firm in 1853, were the Lords Of The Admiralty. During the 'Age of Sail', heavy lifting facilities were not really required by the Navy, but as the 'Age of Steam' dawned, it was obvious that things had to change in order to maintain Britain's supremacy of the high seas. In the 17th and 18th centuries there were six main Royal Navy dockyards in England, at Deptford, Woolwich, Chatham, Sheerness, Portsmouth and Plymouth. All of these were located conveniently for the English Channel, as this offered the best logistic position for engaging the traditional enemies of France and Spain. However, there were also a number of outports in England and Scotland, plus overseas yards, including Gibraltar, Halifax (Nova Scotia) and Jamaica.

Officers at the yards were appointed by the Board of Admiralty, but otherwise the yards were under the administration of the Navy Board, represented at the yard by a resident commissioner. These became very important customers as time progressed and progressive mechanisation was implemented. In the years that followed, they placed substantial orders for all types of equipment with the firm. These ranged from normal items like dockside and floating cranes to the less obvious items like tobacco presses and sugar cane crushing mills. Both these latter items were supplied to Royal Navy establishments in the West Indies, where rum and tobacco were produced to supply the needs of its men.

To cover the entire range of products purchased by the Navy would necessitate a book in its own right, but a large number of official photographs have been deposited on permanent loan to the Royal Naval Museum at Portsmouth.

Left: *A wonderful example of an early swan-neck steam crane supplied to the Devonport Dockyard in the latter part of the 19th-Century. Alongside lays HMS* Queen *a pre-Dreadnought battleship, doyen of the Queen class, which was completed at Devenport in 1904*

Top Right: *This 30-ton floating crane was one of a batch of three similar cranes built in 1929 to order numbers 3850-2. The orders may have been produced for stock, as the order book specifies no customer names. Of the three, No 3850 went to the Royal Navy, No.3851 was purchased by the Avonmouth Harbour Board, whilst No.3852 went to the Port Of London Authority. Carrying a date of 30th January 1930, this picture also shows the stern of the Southampton tug* Princessa, *which can be seen moored just behind the crane's load. On the jetty an armed matelot stands guard whilst talking to a dockyard official in civilian clothing and a bowler hat.*

Bottom Right: *Having been fitted out at the Armstrong works at Elswick, this 150-ton floating crane sets off on its journey down the River Tyne behind an ocean going tug c1920.*

Thanks to its close association with the North East Marine Engineering Company, Cowans Sheldon were able to offer the Royal Navy undoubted levels of experience in marine lifting equipment. Not only did the expertise range from coaling and ship-building cranes, but also to a whole new area of technology. One such area was that seen in the development of floating cranes. Although this is dealt with in some detail in the next chapter, the subject is important enough to mention here in its own right.

When the German Navy began using floating cranes to build bigger and heavier warships, the Royal Navy became extremely concerned. It is therefore no surprise to find that Cowans Sheldon were encouraged to develop an interest in this field in conjunction with the firm of Sir W. G. Armstrong on Tyneside. As a good rail route linked Carlisle to Newcastle, it was feasible to build the cranes in pre-fabricated sections and assemble them on the Tyne. As the new threat to Britain was now being posed by Germany, the North East and Scottish coasts were considered vulnerable, and it was decided to strengthen them by the creation of new naval anchorages. Obviously, the southern dockyard facilities were then in the 'wrong place', but the floating crane offered a strategic alternative, as it could 'attend' to Royal Navy ships whilst they were at anchor.

In the first decade of the 20th Century a number of 'emergency' plans were put into position, and several of these were implemented when war with Germany looked inevitable. There were also plans to create larger dockside cranes for Immingham, Invergordon, Leith and Rosyth. Immingham had its facilities provided by the Great Central Railway for civilian purposes, but much of the equipment was designed with a dual use in mind, and therefore was partially funded by the Navy Board. Of the other locations, only Rosyth was given the full compliment of cranes that had been proposed. A substantial number of new cranes and refurbishment programmes were undertaken for the Naval Dockyards between the wars, but very little business was done by the company in this field after the 1950s.

Top Left: *Portsmouth Dockyard in 1943, showing a travelling crane at one of the dry docks.*

Bottom Left: *In 1927 a new 'standard pattern' travelling dock crane (of all-steel construction) was marketed by Cowans. Order No. 5329 was supplied to Portsmouth Dockyard in 1932.*

Right: *This superb view of a 150-ton floating crane has a Weymouth Class light cruiser as its backdrop (these were built 1910-11 and scrapped 1928-30) and beyond that is a floating dock.*

FLOATING CRANES

Quite when floating cranes became popular in Britain is not precisely known, but by the 1840s considerable numbers were being used in dock and harbour construction. The primary customers were once again the railways who were seeking to increase the efficiency of their facilities where rail goods were trans-shipped on to seagoing or inland waterway vessels.

The first order in the Cowans Sheldon record seems to have been for a 2½-ton floating derrick, which was completed in 1858 on the River Ellen at Maryport but we do not know who the customer was. The next crane was one of 3-tons capacity, and it was sold to a customer in Ireland. Soon there came a spate of orders ranging from the Thames Lighterage Company to the Bombay & Baroda Railway.

Orders were placed by Carlisle & Silloth Bay Dock and Railway Company, the Preston & Wyre Railway, Whitehaven Harbour, the Furness Railway, the Clyde Commission and the North Eastern Railway. At the beginning of the 20th Century, German shipyards began to use floating cranes to build a new generation of battleships and this caused Cowans Sheldon to pay more attention to this business. By 1905 Cowans Sheldon had changed its ideas about 'fixed' cranes, as it saw distinct advantages in high capacity cranes that could be moved around at will. To meet the new ideas, they designed and constructed their first large floating crane in 1906-7, thus changing from small lighterage or civil engineering cranes to ones with a wider commercial application.

Right: *In modernising its floating cranes the Mersey Docks & Harbour Board placed orders for a fleet of new cranes in the 1950s. The 60-ton cranes were given names of strong men from the bible or mythology. Here we see* Sampson *steaming up the Mersey passing the Royal Liver buildings.* Mersey Docks & Harbour Board

Top Right: *This is one of the earliest Cowans Sheldon floating crane pictures to be found, and it features a 3^1/$_2$-ton crane built for the North British Railway in 1870, for the construction of the Tay Bridge. It is pictured during the rebuilding work in 1882, and is typical of the early types that the company supplied up to the end of the 19th-Century.* Dundee City Libraries

Bottom Right: *This 50-ton floating crane is representative of the type of large capacity cranes that were supplied in the first quarter of the 20th Century, with heavier capacities and larger pontoons or hulls on which to float. This one,* Titan II, *is employed in quay improvements on the River Tyne in May 1937. Most of these cranes were not self-propelled and required another vessel to keep them on station during the work.*

In ship-building, the benefit of the high-capacity floating crane was that it enabled really heavy ships to be built without the need to substantially increase or strengthen the capacity of a shipyard's slipways. This allowed a large ship's hull (usually naval vessels) to be constructed on existing slipways, whilst the heavier items such as gun turrets, control masts or towers, armour plate and so on could be made on-shore and then lifted on to the vessel as a complete pre-fabricated sub-assembly by the floating crane.

Naturally, a big customer for floating cranes was the British Government, either through the Crown Agents (who purchased supplies for the colonies) or the Admiralty. The Royal Navy had at least 45 floating cranes (50- to 150-ton capacity) built by Cowans Sheldon and possibly more. During this substantial period of floating crane development and manufacture, a 150-ton crane was ordered by the China & Japan Trading Co.. in 1909 for building Japanese naval vessels at Nagasaki. At this time Japan was considered to be an ally of the British, and it was felt that there was no harm in supplying this type of equipment.

As the world situation worsened, and mobilisation began to build the Admiralty ordered a number of 150-ton floating cranes from Cowans Sheldon. After that, nearly every floating crane ordered for the Royal Naval Dockyards was supplied by the company. Some were sent to 'anchorages' used by the Navy, including those where dry dock or repair facilities were not available; examples of these locations include Bermuda, Hong Kong and Scapa Flow between northern Scotland and Orkney. One of these, a 45-ton crane had to be repaired no less than 15 weeks after it was commissioned, following its running aground near Peterhead (Scotland) whilst on its way to Scapa during World War I.

In 1920, an enquiry came from Japan for another floating crane for , which at 350-tons (when put into service with Mitsubishi in 1933) was the largest floating crane in the world! At this time facilities for building heavy battleships or aircraft carriers were very limited in Japan and nobody in Carlisle could have foreseen the threat the vessels built by these cranes would ultimately pose!

Only two shipyards, the Navy Yard at Kure and Mitsubishi Heavy Industries' yard at Nagasaki were capable of building large ships. Since the Japanese Navy intended to build four Yamato class ships in rapid succession, special preparations for their secret construction had to be made in selected shipyards. Some of these arrangements consisted of expanding dock capacities, building a special transport ship capable of carrying an 18-inch gun turret and hiding such a vessel behind sisal rope curtains for security reasons.

The depth of the building dock at the Kure naval yard, in which the hull of the HIJM *Yamato* was to be laid down in April 1937, was deepened and the capacity of the gantry crane at the dock was increased to 100-tons by Cowans Sheldon. Its secret purpose was to put heavy armour plates in place on a new Japanese warship fleet. These vessels were huge, and at almost 36,000-tons were second only to the RMS *Queen Mary* at 37,387-tons. Needless to say, the launching of a vessel weighing so much raised various problems and the use of floating cranes was considered essential.

Below: *This huge floating crane was built in 1933 for the Mitsubishi company of Japan. Seen off the coast of Honshu island in 1938, I have been unable to discover what happened to this vessel as all my enquiries to Japan on this subject have gone unanswered!*

The four battleships, of which only two were completed, were designed to give Japan supremacy in the Pacific, and were part of a strategy that envisaged the decimation of the American battleship fleet (as was attempted at Pearl Harbor in 1941). Of the four, No. 108 *Yamato* was commissioned in December 1941, just ahead of Japan's unilateral declaration of war. The next, 109 HIJM *Musash* was ready eight months later but after the defeat at Midway, it was recognised that the *Yamato* and the other battleships had no chance to fight without an umbrella of aircraft. Yet it was still the main force for a decisive sea battle with the American fleet, which the Japanese Navy eagerly wanted to have once and for all. On the other hand, a decision was made to convert the No. 110 HIJM *Shinano*, then under construction at Yokosuka Navy Yard into a heavy aircraft carrier.

In mid-1943 the *Musachi* sailed to Truk, where she was joined by the *Yamato*, however they never got a chance to engage the enemy. They were then ordered back to protect the Japanese home waters, but by July 1944 Japan's aircraft carrier power was virtually non-existent, and they were forced to rely solely on the big guns of the battleships. Unprotected, the *Musachi* was sunk in the Sibuyan Sea, south of Luzon, in October 1944 and the *Shinano* was attacked by torpedoes while being moved to Kure for fitting out. Finally, the doyen of the class sank on 7th April 1945 south west of Kyuscho, while on a 'suicide run' to Okinawa.

With the loss of so many big battleships in World War II, including those owned by Britain, France, Germany, Japan and the United States, the conflict finally proved that the era of the big naval vessel was well and truly over; so too was the role of the floating cranes that had been used in their construction. Thereafter more peaceful roles were envisaged for the floating crane, but in other areas too its use went in to decline as the face of the maritime industry began to change, in an area where Cowans Sheldon were undoubtedly one of the World leaders.

In the 1960s and 1970s several new floating cranes were built, but containerisation and the growth of air transport dramatically reduced the demand. Similarly, the decline in the ship-building and repair industry saw the use of floating cranes diminish in that area as well. In recent times the use of huge floating cranes has come back into vogue, especially in specialised marine salvage work.

Top Right: *This crane was purchased by the Southern Railway for Southampton Docks in 1925. It was sent to work on the Clyde during World War II, after trans-Atlantic shipping was transferred there in the war years, and returned to Southampton in 1945. It was given a major overhaul in 1962, withdrawn in 1984 and finally dismantled by a German scrap firm at the Southampton's Eastern Docks in 1985.*

Bottom Right: *Another view of one of the Mersey floating cranes, again the* Sampson, *as it is seen unloading the MV* Montclair *in one of the 'wet docks' sometime in May 1961.* **GEC.**

69

A Miscellany

From the comment made earlier regarding products such as sugar cane mills and tobacco presses, it will be appreciated that Cowans produced a number of diverse miscellanious items. The linking factor was mainly the application of steam, hydraulic or electric power to machinery and equipment that had previously been hand-worked. A few typical examples of the type of ancillary product are seen here, yet the images we have chosen are but a small part of what was a very, very extensive range.

Cowans Sheldon were well known for turntables and cranes, but its ancillary equipment product range is less well-known. Hydraulic wheel-drops, loco-jacks and coach lifting equipment were all sold on a world-wide basis. (A picture of a locomotive wheel drop is shown on page 31). Other examples of the product range included wagon-tipplers, coaling plant and ash disposal equipment. For its maritime customers, a range of capstans, slipways and the like were built, often to special order, to satisfy the customer's special requirements. Quite often 'specials' would be built in order to get the bigger business.

Above: *This book could be filled with images of Cowans Sheldon's non-standard products, but in just two pages these few must suffice. Here was see a trawler slipway built at the LNER's Hull Graving Docks in 1936. It was purchased with government support as part of the preparations for developing civilian infrastructure ahead of World War II.*

Top Right: *The same slipway in May 1962, with MT* Stella Ricel *on the slipway cradle.*

Top Far Right: *At Birkenhead two dock workers use a new 2-ton electric capstan to haul ashore the stern mooring hawser from the bulk carrier MV* William Wheelwright *in 1962. Control of the capstan was by a clutch pedal mounted on the floor plate to the right-hand side of the worker.*

Bottom Right: *A number of hydraulic lifting jacks were supplied to railway carriage workshops all around the world. This particular example went to the Northern Counties (LMS) workshops in Belfast where it is being employed to lift carriage No.518.*

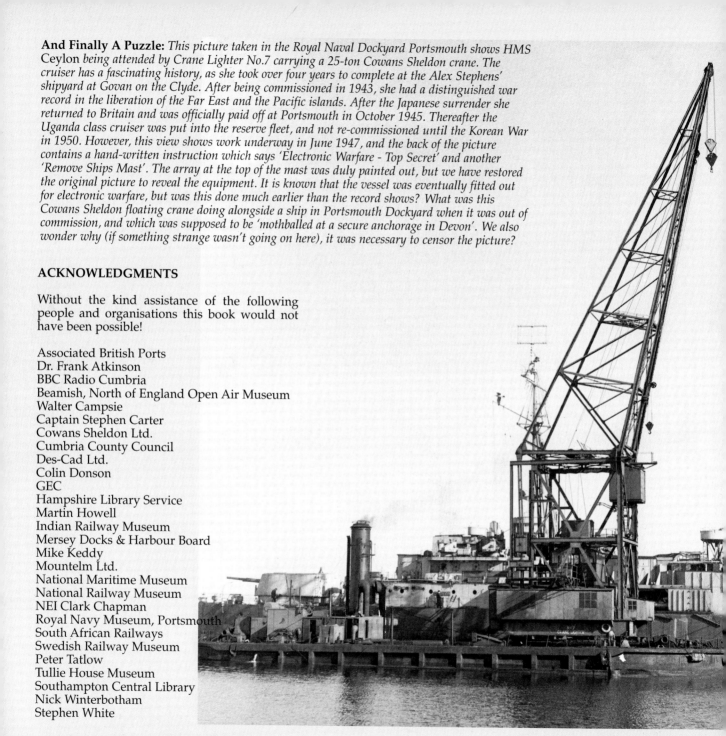

And Finally A Puzzle: *This picture taken in the Royal Naval Dockyard Portsmouth shows HMS Ceylon being attended by Crane Lighter No.7 carrying a 25-ton Cowans Sheldon crane. The cruiser has a fascinating history, as she took over four years to complete at the Alex Stephens' shipyard at Govan on the Clyde. After being commissioned in 1943, she had a distinguished war record in the liberation of the Far East and the Pacific islands. After the Japanese surrender she returned to Britain and was officially paid off at Portsmouth in October 1945. Thereafter the Uganda class cruiser was put into the reserve fleet, and not re-commissioned until the Korean War in 1950. However, this view shows work underway in June 1947, and the back of the picture contains a hand-written instruction which says 'Electronic Warfare - Top Secret' and another 'Remove Ships Mast'. The array at the top of the mast was duly painted out, but we have restored the original picture to reveal the equipment. It is known that the vessel was eventually fitted out for electronic warfare, but was this done much earlier than the record shows? What was this Cowans Sheldon floating crane doing alongside a ship in Portsmouth Dockyard when it was out of commission, and which was supposed to be 'mothballed at a secure anchorage in Devon'. We also wonder why (if something strange wasn't going on here), it was necessary to censor the picture?*

ACKNOWLEDGMENTS

Without the kind assistance of the following people and organisations this book would not have been possible!

Associated British Ports
Dr. Frank Atkinson
BBC Radio Cumbria
Beamish, North of England Open Air Museum
Walter Campsie
Captain Stephen Carter
Cowans Sheldon Ltd.
Cumbria County Council
Des-Cad Ltd.
Colin Donson
GEC
Hampshire Library Service
Martin Howell
Indian Railway Museum
Mersey Docks & Harbour Board
Mike Keddy
Mountelm Ltd.
National Maritime Museum
National Railway Museum
NEI Clark Chapman
Royal Navy Museum, Portsmouth
South African Railways
Swedish Railway Museum
Peter Tatlow
Tullie House Museum
Southampton Central Library
Nick Winterbotham
Stephen White